Uncle Arthur's
BEDTIME STORIES

VOLUME SEVEN

BTS 7-1

COLOR PHOTO BY T. K. MARTIN →

Uncle Arthur is never so happy as when he is in the company of children. Here they are in beautiful Golden Gate Park, San Francisco, California.

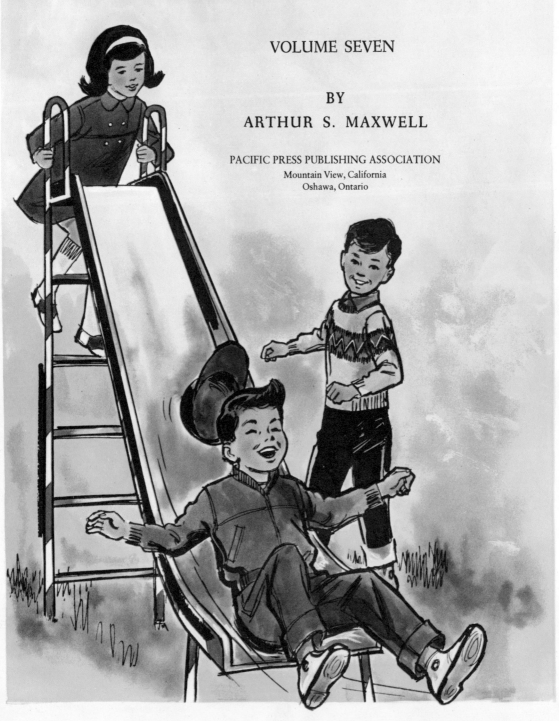

Uncle Arthur's

BEDTIME STORIES

VOLUME SEVEN

BY

ARTHUR S. MAXWELL

PACIFIC PRESS PUBLISHING ASSOCIATION
Mountain View, California
Oshawa, Ontario

CONTENTS

Lesson Index

Artists participating in the illustration of this volume are: Harry Anderson, Robert Berran, Harry Baerg, Siegfried Bohlmann, Thomas Dunbebin, Harvey Fuller, John Gourley, Arlo Greer, Russell Harlan, Gedge Harman, William Heaslip, Iris Johnson, Manning de V. Lee, David Neal, Don Nelson, Vernon Nye, Clyde Provonsha, Peter J. Rennings, and Herbert Rudeen.

The House That Glowed

It was Christmas Eve, and poor little Johann, driven out of his home by an angry and brutal step-father, was trudging wearily through the snow.

His ragged coat was sodden with melted snow. His shoes were split at the seams, so that his feet were damp and numb with cold. His quaint cap, pulled well down over his ears and forehead, had a gaping tear that let in the biting wind.

Night was falling, and the gathering darkness found the homeless little boy still plodding on his sad and lonely way.

"If only I could find some shelter, some place where I could get warm, and the wind would not chill me so," he thought to himself. "If only someone would give me some food to eat and something hot to drink!"

Coming to the edge of the forest, he caught sight of a little village nestling in the valley below, with several fine, large houses dotting the hills around it. Lights were already twinkling in the windows, while the smoke from many chimneys, curling upward, blended with the murky sky.

A great new hope sprang up in little Johann's heart. Here

9

Johann was homeless, tired, hungry, and discouraged as he trudged out into the night and stood before a little old cottage with a light in it.

at last, among so many lovely homes, he would surely find someone to care for him. He walked more quickly, certain that his troubles were almost over.

Soon he came to the entrance of a fine, big mansion. There were many lights in the windows and a very bright one over the front door. "Surely," he thought, "people who could live in such a house must have lots of money and would be only too pleased to help a poor, hungry little boy."

Very bravely he walked up to the front door, and by standing on tiptoe, managed to reach the bell. He pushed it hard, and there was such a noise inside that it frightened him. But he was more frightened still when the great oak door was thrown back and a big man dressed in a fine blue and gold uniform looked out at him.

"Did you ring that bell?" asked the haughty butler, frowning.

"Y-y-y-yes," stammered Johann, "I-I-I'm very cold and hungry, and I thought you——"

"This is Christmas Eve," snapped the butler, "and the house is full of guests. I'm sorry, but we haven't time to bother with the likes of you just now. Good night."

And the door was shut.

"Oh!" said Johann to himself, "I never thought anyone would do that. But perhaps they are too busy here. I must try somewhere else."

So he walked on down into the village itself, passing by the other big mansions for fear the people inside might also be too busy to care about a hungry little boy on Christmas Eve.

10

From the first house he reached there came sounds of music and laughter. "These people will be friendly," he said to himself as he knocked gently on the door. But there was so much noise inside that he had to knock again and again, each time louder than before.

At last the door swung open, and a young man wearing a funny paper cap looked out.

"Excuse me," said Johann, "but I wondered if you could——"

"Sorry," cried the gay young man, "we're having a great Christmas Eve party in here, and we can't stop now."

"But please, please!" pleaded Johann.

"Sorry. Good night!" cried the young man. And bang! The door was shut.

Terribly disappointed, Johann went next door, but the people there were making so much noise that they didn't even hear him at all, loud as he knocked.

At the next house a crabby old gentleman looked out an upstairs window and told him to run home and not bother the neighbors. Run home, indeed!

At another house he was told to call again another day. They would help him then perhaps, the people said. But he needed help now!

So, going from house to house through the entire village, he sought shelter and food, and found none.

Almost hopeless and heartbroken, he trudged on

into the night, leaving the twinkling lights behind him. He felt he could lie down and die in the road, he was so tired, so hungry, so discouraged.

Just then he happened to look up and found himself passing a tiny, tumble-down old cottage, so dark and dismal that he probably wouldn't have seen it at all but for the white carpet of snow on the ground showing it up. A blind almost covered the one window letting a faint streak of light show through at the bottom.

Johann stood still and wondered what he should do.

Should he knock here?

What would be the use? Surely if the people who lived in all the big houses—who had money for lovely parties and things—couldn't afford to help a poor boy, how could the folks in a house like this? No, it was of no use. Better not bother them. Better go on and die in the woods.

Then he thought again. He had knocked at so many houses, there could be no harm in trying one more. So he turned from the road up the snow-covered garden path and tapped gently on the door.

A moment later the door opened cautiously, and an elderly woman peered out. "Bless my soul!" she exclaimed. "Whatever are you doing out there in the cold tonight?"

"Please——" began Johann.

But before he could say another word she had flung the door wide open and dragged him inside.

"You poor little child!" she exclaimed. "Deary, deary me! You look so cold and hungry. Half starved, or I'm mistaken. And wet through. Let's get those things off at once. Wait a moment while I stir up the fire and put the kettle on."

12

Johann looked about him and saw that the little one-roomed cottage was as bare as could be, without even a carpet on the floor. The light he had seen came from one lone candle set on the mantelpiece. But he hadn't time to see much else, for the kind woman was soon stripping off his wet rags, wrapping him in a blanket, and setting him up at the table before a bowl of steaming soup.

Then she went back to stir the pot on the stove. As she did so she suddenly noticed that something strange was happening. She looked up.

Was it a dream, or were her eyes deceiving her? The candle-light had given place to a warm and lovely glow that seemed to be getting brighter every minute, filling every corner of the cottage with a heavenly radiance. Every drab piece of furniture seemed to be shining and glistening like burnished gold, as when God filled the temple with His glory.

And the rich man, looking down from his mansion on the hill, suddenly exclaimed, "There's a strange light in the valley. Look! Widow Greatheart's cottage is on fire!"

The news spread swiftly from house to house, and soon all the gay parties were abandoned as the people, wrapping themselves up in their coats and shawls, rushed out to see what was the matter.

They saw the light, too, and running toward the widow's cottage, beheld the poor tumble-down old building glowing like an alabaster bowl. Very excited, they gathered around it.

Peering inside, all they could see was the dear old woman caring for the very same little boy who had called that night at all their homes.

Then, as the light faded, they knocked on the door to ask anxiously what could have happened.

"I really do not know," said Widow Greatheart, with a smile of wondrous joy and satisfaction on her face. "I just seemed to hear a voice saying to me, 'Inasmuch as you have done it unto one of the least of these My children, you have done it unto Me.'"

PAINTING BY HARRY BAERG

Little Missionary

There are two things that you should know about Betty. First, when this wonderful event happened, she was just about eight years old. Second, she had a smile "like the smile of an angel." And that must be a very lovely smile, I should say.

Oh, yes, there was something else about her that you should know. She loved to do "missionary work," as she called it. Every chance she had she would go out on the streets of the city in which she lived and give away tracts and papers and little bound portions of Scripture which told of the love of Jesus. So sweetly did she smile up at the people that they couldn't help taking a tract from her. She was so very, very pleasant and friendly that they just had to take one.

Then one Sunday afternoon as Betty was walking along, smiling away at everybody as she handed out her "missionary papers," she suddenly looked ahead and saw something that for a moment made her very frightened. A drunk man was staggering along toward her on the sidewalk.

16

Now, most little girls—and some little boys—would run away from a drunk man. But not Betty. She was a brave little girl. She was doing "missionary work for Jesus," and she would not be turned back.

So very boldly she went up to the drunk man, and smiling her lovely angel smile, held up a little pocket Gospel.

He stopped and looked at her.

"May I give you this little book?" she asked.

"W-w-what little book?" he said gruffly.

"This little book," said Betty, holding the little Gospel higher still. "And please, sir, it will do you lots of good."

The drunk man, moved by Betty's sweet little face and lovely smile, took the book in his hand.

"H-h-how much is it?" he stuttered.

"Oh, nothing at all, please, sir," said Betty. "I just want you to read it. And really, it *will* do you lots of good."

The poor man slipped the book into his pocket.

Betty passed on, and for a moment the man stood there speechless. Then he, too, went on his way. But he could not get the little girl out of his mind. That angel smile fascinated him.

After a while he took the little book out of his coat pocket and began to read. It was a tiny copy of the Gospel of John.

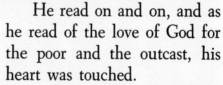

He read on and on, and as he read of the love of God for the poor and the outcast, his heart was touched.

"God so loved the world," he read, "that He gave His only begotten Son, that whosoever

believeth in Him should not perish, but have everlasting life."

Farther on he found this beautiful promise: "Whatsoever ye shall ask in My name, that will I do, that the Father may be glorified in the Son. If ye shall ask any thing in My name, I will do it." John 14:13, 14.

Then he read: "If ye love Me, keep My commandments. And I will pray the Father, and He shall give you another Comforter, that He may abide with you for ever." Verses 15, 16.

At last he turned his eyes to heaven and prayed that God would forgive him for all his sins and help him to live a better life.

He was converted. He went to church, and was baptized.

Exactly one year after he met Betty, I met him. He was then the deacon of a large church in California. He told me that before Betty smiled at him and gave him that little book, he had no work, no home, no money—nothing at all.

Now he is happy and prosperous, and all his needs are supplied.

What a beautiful thing it was that Betty did! And what a wonderful star she will have in her crown one day for bringing this soul to Jesus!

God bless all little girls, and all little boys, too, who go out to do "missionary work" like this.

Finders

Keepers

Jessie was so excited when she came in to dinner that she could hardly speak.

"Mamma, look what I've found!" she panted.

"Whatever do you have there?" exclaimed Mamma. "Why, it looks like a purse."

"Yes, it is," cried Jessie. "It's just the dearest little purse, and there's a lot of money in it, too. Just think what I'll be able to buy with it."

"Let me see it," said Mamma, taking the purse and looking inside. "You're right, Jessie. There is quite a lot of money in it —nearly four dollars."

"Oh!" cried Jessie, mouth wide open and eyes sparkling.

"But you wouldn't want to keep this yourself, would you?" asked Mamma.

"Why not?" asked Jessie, a trace of fear in her voice. "Remember, finders keepers."

"Sometimes in a game, perhaps," said Mamma, "but not with somebody else's purse. Why, just think! Perhaps some poor woman dropped it on her way to do some shopping, and

19

this money may be all she had to provide for her family the rest of the week."

"But, Mamma, I found it."

"I know you did, dear, but she lost it, and it's really still hers, at least until you've tried every way you know how to find her. You want to think how you would feel if you lost your purse and somebody found it, and kept it. You wouldn't like that, would you?"

"I hadn't thought of that," said Jessie. "I don't suppose I would like it."

"I don't think you would either," said Mamma, "and if we are going to do unto others as we want them to do unto us ——"

"I suppose I'd better take it back," interrupted Jessie. "But what shall I do with it?"

"The proper thing is to take it to the police station," said Mamma, "and they will keep it there and see if anybody comes for it. If not, then they will give it back to you."

"All right, then," said Jessie, smiling. "I'll take it right away. That poor woman is probably worrying herself sick about it."

So off she ran as fast as she could go.

On the way she met a school friend.

"What's the hurry?" asked Marjorie.

"Oh, I found a purse in the street, and I'm just taking it to the police station."

"Any money in it?"

"Four dollars."

"Then you're going the wrong way," said Marjorie. "Why don't you keep it?"

20

"Oh, I couldn't," said Jessie. "Some poor woman may be in a dreadful state about it, and I want to get it back to her as soon as I can."

"You are stupid," said Marjorie. "Why should you worry about that, I'd like to know?"

"Maybe I am stupid," said Jessie, a little worried, "but I'm going to take it anyway."

At the police station Jessie told how she had found the purse. The policeman beamed on her, and said he thought she was the most honest girl in town. Then he made a note of her name and address and the nature and contents of the bag. This done, Jessie left feeling as happy as if someone had given her a million dollars.

And that was not the end of her joy.

That night there was a knock at the front door, and Jessie, opening it, recognized the minister's wife, one of her best friends.

"Jessie," said the visitor, "I've just found my purse at the police station, and the policeman on duty told me that it was you who took it in. I want to thank you ever so much, and

maybe you would let me give you something to show you how very grateful I am."

"Oh, no, no, no!" exclaimed Jessie. "I wouldn't dream of it. Please don't! I'm so happy to have helped you and that you have your purse back again. I had no idea that it could possibly have belonged to you, or I would have brought it straight to your home."

"I know you would," said the minister's wife. "And I do want you to know, Jessie, how very much I appreciate what you did. I shall never forget it."

When her visitor had gone, Jessie looked at Mamma, and a strange, understanding smile came over both their faces.

"What a fortunate thing it was that I took it back," said Jessie. "Just suppose I had gone to church with that purse in my hand! It makes me go hot and cold all over just to think of it. And if I had spent her money, I never could have forgiven myself."

"Well," said Mamma, shaking her head, "it's just one more proof that it always pays to do right."

Why the World Felt Sad

All the world felt sad when King Edward VIII gave up his throne.

For days before it happened, people scarcely talked of anything else. The story filled the newspapers in every land on earth.

In busy cities, faraway villages, dreary deserts, it was the one topic of conversation.

At an isolated garage in the lonely wilderness of Arizona the first question I was asked was not, "How much gasoline do you want?" but, "What of the king?"

Everywhere it was the same. In churches, in schools, in hotels, in restaurants, in stores, always I met the same anxious inquiry, "What of the king?"

And when he spoke the final word of abdication, a hush seemed to fall upon mankind. In some places business ceased for the day.

Why did men love him so? More than anything else, I think, it was due to his thoughtfulness for others. He was always kind and sympathetic; and there was something about his friend-

liness toward everybody, and particularly his genuine interest in the common people, that won the affection of all—Englishmen, Australians, Canadians, South Africans, Americans, and people of all tongues and climes.

Do you remember that lovely thing he did just before the *Queen Mary* was launched on the Clyde?

It is said that he walked seven miles that day, up and down that wonderful vessel, inspecting every part of her from the engine room to the bridge. Then when he had finished, and everybody thought he would be tired and ready to go back home, to the amazement and concern of his private detectives, he made his way through the crowd and began to visit the homes of the

workers who live near the docks. Their homes are not the sort royalty usually visit, but that made no difference to the young king.

In and out of the houses he went, talking with the astonished mothers and children. "If it is right to visit the *Queen Mary*," he said, "it is surely right to visit the people who made her."

When the story appeared in the papers next day, you could almost feel the thrill of delight that swept over the country.

Which reminds me of another kindly act of his when he was Prince of Wales.

He had been asked to visit a private hospital for crippled soldiers. Arriving there on the appointed day, he went from one to another of the poor, suffering men, speaking some cheering word to each of them and encouraging all by his presence. On reaching the door, he was about to leave, when he inquired whether he had seen all the patients.

"No," was the reply, "there are seven others, but they are so seriously disfigured that we felt you might not wish to see them."

"I must see them," said the prince.

At this he was ushered into the sanctuary of exceptional suffering. Going quietly from bed to bed, he spoke in kind, gentle tones to each man, thanking him for all he had done for England.

Again he was leaving, when he said to his guide, "You said there were seven men, and I have seen only six. Where is the other?"

"Your Highness," was the reply, "nobody can see this man, he is so terribly maimed—disfigured out of the likeness of humanity."

"I must see him also," said the prince.

"Better not, sir; it is terrible."

"Still, I wish to see him."

They went in together, the prince, very pale, walking firmly to the bedside. With bowed head he looked down upon this poor wreck of humanity, that could neither see nor hear him.

Then, very slowly, he stooped and kissed the man's face. It was the highest homage he could pay, and surely the most gracious act a king of England ever did.

No wonder the whole world loved King Edward VIII, and sorrowed as he left his throne.

As king he may be forgotten, but as a friend of the people he will be loved forever.

Love begets love, and it is deeds like these—humble, thoughtful, gentle, generous—that win the hearts of men.

The Wrong Key

Henry was getting angrier and angrier. On the table in front of him was a small black box given him by his father, in which he used to keep his most precious things, so that his little brothers would not tamper with them.

It was locked, and Henry was trying to unlock it.

But it just wouldn't unlock.

He tried and tried and tried, but all in vain.

He pushed the key in and pulled it out—and pushed it in again, turning it this way and that. Still nothing happened.

He banged and shook the box and turned it upside down and back again, but without result.

He was in a hurry. He had promised to meet a friend downtown half an hour ago; but the stamps he was to take with him were in the box. Still in the box! Why wouldn't it open?

Mother came in, sympathetic as usual.

"What's the matter?" she asked.

"This box!" snapped Henry. "It just won't open."

"Let me try," said Mother.

"No use," said Henry. "I've tried over and over again."

28

"Maybe you have the wrong key," suggested Mother gently.

"No, I haven't," growled Henry angrily; "surely I should know the key to my own box."

"You should," said Mother, "but everybody makes mistakes sometimes."

"Well, I haven't," growled Henry. "Yet it won't open. Oh, dear!"

Mother withdrew.

Henry went on turning the key.

At last, in fierce impatience, he seized a pair of pliers and gave it an added twist.

Of course, it broke in the lock.

"There! Now I can't open it at all," he cried, tears coming into his eyes.

Suddenly he caught sight of his hammer.

"I *will* get it open," he said, "whatever happens."

A moment later the house echoed to the sound of heavy blows.

Bang, bang, bang!

"Got it!" he whispered, as the lock burst and the lid sprang open.

"What have you done?" cried Mother, as she ran into the room.

"Done?" said Henry. "Opened the box, of course."

"You have," said Mother, "and you'll never shut it again. See, it is broken beyond repair. And that box cost six dollars."

"Did it?" exclaimed Henry, amazed.

30

"Indeed it did," said Mother, "and it will cost you all that to get another one."

"Phew!" said Henry, beginning to regret his impatience.

"By the way," said Mother, picking up a small, shining object from the floor, "what's this?"

"That? That's the right key to the box," said Henry in dismay. "I must have had the wrong one in the lock all the time. Why *didn't* I see it? And now my box is all smashed!"

"You know," said Mother quietly, "it never does pay to lose one's patience. We always make mistakes when we do."

Henry said nothing, but as he hurried down the street to meet his friend, he thought seriously.

It will be a long time, I should say, before he does such a foolish thing again.

Helping Daddy

Daddy was down in the garden, putting some seeds in the ground. They were pea seeds, and Daddy was making a straight row so that when the peas came up they would look nice.

Mabel was watching Daddy, and she thought that she would like to sow some pea seeds too.

So she got her little spade and dug a hole in the ground. Then she came to Daddy and said, "Please, Daddy, give me some of your pea seeds for me to sow."

So Daddy gave her some of his pea seeds, and Mabel dropped them into the big hole she had made and covered them over with earth. Daddy looked around to see what she was doing, and he said, "Why, my little girl, those seeds are too far down. They will never be able to find their way up."

"Well," said Mabel, "I 'specks they will grow all right, but I think I will sow some more in case they don't."

But Daddy had already used all the pea seeds, and Mabel was very much disappointed. And do you know what she did? You could never guess.

32

Well, when Daddy wasn't looking, she went over to where he had planted his row of peas, and poking her hands down into the earth, brought up some of the seeds. Just then Daddy looked round and said, "Oh, you naughty little girl! What are you doing?"

"Just getting some more seeds," said Mabel, " 'cos I didn't have enough."

"Well, I never!" said Daddy. "Digging up my nice new row of seeds. That is naughty of you, Mabel."

"But they will grow just as well here as there," said Mabel, digging another deep hole and dropping in the seeds she had taken from Daddy's row.

"No, they won't," said Daddy. "You mustn't take seeds that do not belong to you. If you had left them where they were, we

should have had some lovely peas from them someday. But now they will never grow."

Later in the spring, Daddy and Mabel were down in the garden again.

"What a lovely row of peas!" said Mabel.

"Yes," said Daddy. "But it's spoiled by a little gap at the other end, isn't it?"

"Yes," said Mabel. "Is that where I took some out?"

"Yes," said Daddy, "and where are they now?"

"I can't see them anywhere," said Mabel.

"No," said Daddy, "and you never will. Nobody ever gains by doing naughty things. I think they must have gone down the other way."

Maybe they had.

34

The Letter to Mamma

Mamma was very ill, and some people had come in a strange car with a red cross on it and carried her away to the hospital.

Poor little Ted and Tod were very sad and lonely. They had never felt so lonely before. How they did long for Mamma to come home again! Every time a car went by, they would run to the window to see whether the car with the red cross on it had come back. Poor little Tod cried himself to sleep every night.

"Mamma said we were to write to her often," said Ted one day. "Shall we do it now?"

Tod said, "Yes," and they set to work. Tod found some paper and a bottle of ink. When he opened the ink bottle, the stopper ran around all over the paper and made a big black mark. So they decided to write the letter in pencil.

"Mamma won't mind the blots, I expect," said Ted. "Now, what shall we say?"

"Tell her I want her to come back soon," said Tod.

"I will," said Ted.

So they wrote, and here is the letter:

Dear Darling mother?

Please come back soon.
We hope you are getting
better. We love you so
much. We want you home
home again. Tod has lost
a button off his coat.
You must not get sick
again. Pussy has got some
kittens. We say our pra-
yers every night. We
ask Jesus to make you
better. Tod say come back
soon and so do I.
With lots of love and
kisses from your lovely boys

Tod and Ted.

And then they sealed the envelope, got a stamp from Auntie, and went out to put the letter in the mailbox.

Tod said he wanted to mail the letter, but when they got to the box they found he could not quite reach the place where the letters go in. So Ted lifted Tod as high as he could, and Tod poked the letter into the box.

And when Mamma opened the letter the next morning she was so pleased she said she felt better already.

Why Mary Cheered Up

There," said Mary, flinging her school satchel down on the kitchen table, "I'm never going to try again."

"Why, Mary dear, what has happened?" asked Mother. "You were so happy when you went off to school this morning."

"Maybe I was," replied Mary sadly, "but I'm not now."

"But why, dear?"

"Teacher put up the examination results today, and I'm twelfth again. I did so want to be at the top this time."

Mary buried her face in her hands and began to cry.

"Cheer up," said Mother, coming over to Mary's side and putting one arm around her. "It might have been much worse, you know. Why, you might have been at the bottom, and that would have been terrible, wouldn't it?"

"I suppose it would," said Mary, "but I'm never anything else but twelfth. I simply can't get to the top. I've never had a prize, and I suppose I never shall. I am just a dull, stupid dunce, that's what I am, and I shall never be any good at all."

"Why, Mary dear, you don't need to worry. There are some subjects in which you have had nearly perfect marks. Didn't you get ninety-five per cent in botany the other day? That should cheer you up."

"It doesn't. Nothing could ever cheer me up," wailed Mary.

"Let me tell you a story, then," said Mother. "You've heard of Mr. Baldwin, once prime minister of England?"

"I'm not sure," said Mary.

"Well, do you know, when he was a boy and took the entrance examination at the famous school known as Harrow, he failed?"

"Did he?" said Mary.

"He surely did," said Mother. "And another boy who failed in that same examination was called Freddie Smith. When he grew up he became Lord Birkenhead, one of the greatest lawyers of his time."

"Perhaps there's hope for me yet," said Mary, brightening up a little.

"Let me tell you some more," continued Mother. "You've heard of Clive of India. Teacher may have mentioned him at school sometime."

"Yes."

"Well, it is said of him that he was the despair of his teachers. As for Nelson, the great admiral, when he went to school, he was a very poor scholar. I don't suppose his teacher ever thought he would win Trafalgar or the battle of the Nile."

"I don't suppose he did," said Mary.

"Then there is Sir Ernest Shackleton," went on Mother, "that noble explorer who went to the South Pole. You would hardly believe it, Mary, but as a boy he never rose high in his school, and couldn't apply himself to his books at all."

"Fancy all those great men being like me," said Mary, a smile beginning to curl around the corners of her mouth, and a merry twinkle showing in her eye.

"There are many more people like you, dear. Abraham Lincoln himself had a big struggle when he was young. Nobody in those days dreamed that he would ever be President of the United States."

"Well!" exclaimed Mary. "I thought all these great people were always at the top in school."

"It's a strange thing," said Mother, "but few of them were. Many of the most useful men who have ever lived simply couldn't get on well at school. Being at the top in school doesn't mean that you are going to be at the top in everything all your life."

"But the top girls and boys seem so bright," said Mary; "they always get good marks and can answer so much more quickly than I can."

"Yes," said Mother, "but remember the tortoise and the hare. It isn't always the fastest that gets there first."

"I'm sure I'm as slow as a tortoise, anyway," said Mary.

"Then cheer up and keep on pegging away," said Mother. "You're bound to win someday if you do."

"Oh, well," said Mary, springing to her feet with new hope in her heart. "I suppose I'll have to try a bit harder next time." And she did.

A Tale of Two Sparrows

Mr. and Mrs. Sparrow were just married, and they were looking for a nice place where they could build their nest.

They flew about for a long time without any success. Mrs. Sparrow was rather hard to please. Whenever Mr. Sparrow found a nice little corner that he thought would do, and came swooping down through the air to tell her so, Mrs. Sparrow would say, "Oh, that's not at all suitable for me, Mr. Sparrow. I must have something much better than that for my home."

At last Mr. Sparrow got so discouraged that he said he wouldn't look any more, and that Mrs. Sparrow, if she were so particular, had better look for herself.

Mrs. Sparrow took him at his word and said that if she couldn't find a nice place in half the time that Mr. Sparrow had taken, she would know the reason why.

So off flew Mrs. Sparrow to see what she could do.

In a little while she returned.

"I've found a wonderful place," she said. "It's warm and cozy, well protected from the weather, and the way in is so small that no one else will ever be able to find it; so we shall be quite by ourselves, with no neighbors to annoy us. You'll be able to sleep late in the morning, for there will be no other birds around to start singing too early."

"My dear!" cried Mr. Sparrow, "where can it be? Do show me at once. I'm so glad you have been so successful."

"Ah," said Mrs. Sparrow, "it takes me to find a home. I'll show you. You come along with me."

With that Mrs. Sparrow hopped off her perch and flew high in the air, with Mr. Sparrow following meekly at a respectful distance behind.

On and on they flew.

"Where are you taking me?" asked Mr. Sparrow, getting alarmed.

"You'll find out in a minute," said Mrs. Sparrow.

They were approaching a lofty church tower, and Mrs. Sparrow seemed to be flying to the very top of it.

"My dear, do be careful," called Mr. Sparrow. "This is very dangerous."

Mrs. Sparrow flew on as if she had not heard him. At last she alighted where a small window had been broken near the top of the tower. In a moment she had popped inside and looked around.

Poor Mr. Sparrow followed, very much alarmed and wondering what terrible thing would happen to them.

"Look," said Mrs. Sparrow. "Isn't this ideal? The very thing we have been looking for! Dry, fairly clean, and very private. I told you, Mr. Sparrow, that I would find the right place."

"But, my dear," said poor Mr. Sparrow, greatly agitated, "do you think it's all right? Is it safe?"

"Safe!" cried Mrs. Sparrow. "Of course it's safe. Now please get busy and bring all the straw you can find. We might as well make ourselves comfortable as soon as we can."

Very meekly Mr. Sparrow obeyed. In a little while he was back again, bringing a few pieces of straw in his beak. By this time Mrs. Sparrow had selected an attractive spot for the nest in between a number of wooden pipes. Mr. Sparrow put down his pieces of straw and went out in search of more.

It did not take them very long to build their nest, and in a day or two they were settled down, ready to enjoy a well-earned rest.

44

All at once something terrible happened. It was on a Wednesday evening about seven o'clock. Mr. and Mrs. Sparrow were settled comfortably in bed when suddenly they were awakened by a terrific noise. Groans and roars came from the big pipes, whines and shrieks from the little pipes. The whole place rocked and shook.

"My dear! My dear!" cried Mr. Sparrow. "What's the matter? What can have happened? Are you safe?"

But Mrs. Sparrow was not there to hear. Already she was at the broken window, shrieking at Mr. Sparrow to escape for his life. Without another thought they both jumped from the top of the tower out into the dark, cold night.

Probably those poor little sparrows will never know what really happened that terrible evening. As long as they live they will tell their friends how they lost their beautiful home, recounting in awed whispers the terrors they suffered in the haunted tower.

The fact was, of course, that they had merely tried to make their nest in the church organ loft. And the awful

sounds they had heard that Wednesday evening were really the hymns the organist was playing for the prayer meeting.

To the people in the church the music was beautiful. "How lovely!" they all had said. "What delightful harmonies! What a wonderful organist!"

But to the poor little sparrows in the loft it had seemed like an earthquake and a hurricane combined.

All of which proves that things are not always what they seem. Sometimes children, like the sparrows, are frightened merely because they do not understand. Sometimes, too, they grumble and growl because they are not yet old enough to appreciate the meaning of things beyond them.

Perhaps you have heard a little boy say sometime, "I don't like going to church. I never can understand a word the preacher says, and some of the hymns have no tune to them at all." Someday, however, he will understand the preacher and rejoice in his inspiring words. Someday the hymns that have seemed to have the least tune in them will be loved and prized most of all.

Perhaps, too, you have heard a little girl say, "I don't know why I have to put up with so much. I don't have the nice things other children have."

That *is* hard to understand, I admit. But when you feel like that, just think that Someone is playing on the organ of your life. To you the notes sound harsh and discordant, but the Organist knows what He is playing, and someday you will understand how lovely was the tune that He composed.

So when things go wrong and you are tempted to judge quickly and unkindly, just wait a little while and think of the sparrows in the tower.

47

When we let Him, Jesus composes the discordant notes of our life into a beautiful harmony.

Back From the Sea

Nellie and Frankie were on their way to the beach for the afternoon. How happy they were! There was nothing they loved so much as playing in the sand or paddling in the warm, shallow water.

"Now let me remind you both of just one thing," said Daddy as the car slowed down. "Remember that you are both wearing new shoes. Take them off as soon as you get on the beach, and be very careful not to lose them."

"Yes, Daddy!" they cried. "We will." But their thoughts were far away— on the beautiful wavelets which were breaking softly on the shore.

The car stopped, the door opened, and out jumped the two excited children, who ran off toward the water at top speed.

As they reached the sand, Nellie remembered about her shoes, and taking them off, carefully laid them where she was sure she would be able to find them again. Frankie, however, in his eagerness to reach the ocean, quite forgot all about his promise until he was right down near the water. Then because he thought it was too far to go back, he just kicked off his shoes and

socks, left them where they fell, and dashed on into the surf.

What a wonderful time they had together! When they had paddled long enough, they built sand castles, ran races, then paddled some more. So busy were they with their play that they failed to notice the turn of the tide, or how the waves crept slowly but surely up the beach to where Frankie's precious new shoes were lying. But the waves came on just the same.

By and by, all too soon, Daddy called from far up the beach, "It's time to go home; we'll have to be going soon."

Then began the search for the shoes. Nellie found hers all right, because she had been careful to leave them in a safe place. But Frankie's shoes were nowhere to be found. In fact, he

couldn't even find the place where he had left them. It was covered by the water!

They searched and searched, but it was no use. The shoes were not to be found. Daddy said that Frankie was a very careless little boy, and he would have to go home barefooted. But Nellie said that she had a pair of slippers in the car and Frankie could wear them.

So that is how they returned home, Nellie in her shiny new shoes and Frankie in Nellie's slippers.

Frankie did not feel very happy about it, for he liked new shoes just as much as Nellie. And you can be quite sure that

Daddy did not feel happy about it, nor Mother either, for they would have to find the money for another pair.

"Maybe we could go back in the morning," said Daddy, "and have another look."

"What's the use?" said Mother. "They will have been washed out in the ocean by now."

"Well, we might as well go," said Daddy. "It won't do any harm to look once more."

So in the morning they all drove back to the beach again to search for Frankie's shoes.

This time, strangely enough, it was Daddy and Mother who got out of the car, while Nellie and Frankie remained inside. They said they wanted to stay behind a little while by themselves, but didn't say why. This was so unusual that Daddy said they could if they wished; then he and Mother started off without them.

Left alone, Nellie and Frankie knelt down by the back seat of the car and began to pray. Nellie, by the way, was just nine and Frankie, seven. But they believed that Jesus loves children and delights to help them when they get into trouble.

So together they sent up a little prayer that Frankie's lost shoes might be found! Six times they prayed the same prayer, over and over again.

Then they saw Daddy and Mother hurrying back to the car. They were smiling happily as though they had had good fortune.

They had.

"Look!" cried Nellie. "See what Daddy has!"

"My shoes! My shoes!" cried Frankie.

Yes, there they were, and hardly damaged at all. Daddy had found them not a hundred yards from where he had stopped the

51

car. How or why they happened to be just there, no one could tell, but everybody was thankful, especially Nellie and Frankie, who then told what they had been doing while Daddy and Mother were on the beach searching for the shoes.

Such a little thing to pray for, you say? I know. Just a pair of shoes! But why not? Jesus is interested in all the little things of our lives. Did He not say of the sparrow: "Not one of them is forgotten before God"? He did, and He added, too: "Ye are of more value than many sparrows." Luke 12:6, 7.

So we are not to hesitate to pray for little things as well as for big things. Not one of our prayers—not a single one—is "forgotten before God."

52

Barbara's Talent

"Mother!" gasped Barbara, rushing into the dining room and flopping down in an armchair, "I've got to earn some money."

"My dear!" exclaimed Mother. "Whatever is the matter with the child now!"

"Yes, I must," went on Barbara. "It's most important, and I have got to earn a lot very quickly."

Mother began to look serious.

"What for?" she asked.

"Well," said Barbara very excitedly, "Mr. Walters, the new superintendent, told us in Sabbath school this morning that if we didn't give $250 for missions within the next two weeks, Mr. James would have to come back from India right away."

"Why, we've only just sent him out," said Mother.

"I know; that's just the trouble," said Barbara. "Mr. Walters said that everybody thought there would be enough money to keep him there. But there isn't. Something's gone wrong, he said, and the Mission Board is very hard up. So there, if we don't raise the $250 in two weeks, well, Mr. James comes home."

53

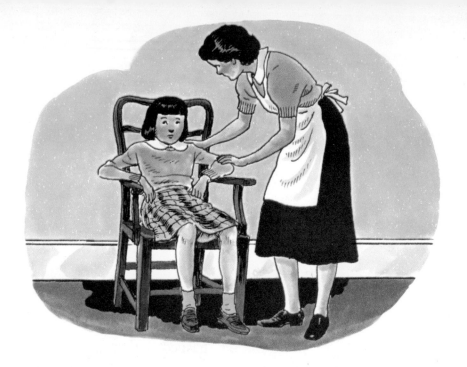

"That sounds very serious," said Mother. "But Barbara dear, *we* can't raise $250 in just two weeks."

"Oh, no," said Barbara, "not we by ourselves. Each class has agreed to raise $25. Each one in the class has promised to raise $2.50."

"Have you promised $2.50, Barbara?" gasped Mother.

"Why, of course," said Barbara. "I couldn't do anything else, could I? And that's why I've got to earn some money. How can I do it, Mother dear?"

"Well," said Mother, "it's all very well for you to promise money like that, but I haven't got it to give you, dear, even if you help me ever so much. You know Daddy has not been earning much lately."

"I know," said Barbara, on the verge of tears, "but I—surely can—earn it—somehow. Er—er—I must keep my promise, now that I've made it."

Barbara began to cry.

"Never mind, dear," said Mother, "we'll find some way out, surely. But you have taken on a difficult task, and no mistake."

"I did so want to help," said Barbara.

"I'm sure you did," said Mother, putting her arms around Barbara's neck. "Let's think it over a while and see what can be done."

That evening, as the family gathered around the fire for prayers, Mother read to them the parable of the Talents. As the story proceeded, Barbara's face grew more and more serious. She could see the man with the five talents trading with them and earning five talents more to give to the King. Then she saw the man with the two talents earning two talents. And then at last she saw the man with one talent burying it in the earth and having nothing—nothing—nothing!—to give to the Lord at His return.

She became very solemn.

"What's troubling you, dear?" asked Mother as she closed the Book.

"Oh, I feel just like the man with one talent who didn't earn anything at all. Only there's just this difference, that I don't have even *one* talent."

"Well, Barbara, I didn't think you would take it so much to heart. And you have talents, many of them."

"No, I haven't. I haven't any at all. I'm just no good, and I'll never be able to earn that money."

"Oh, Barbara, don't be so sad. You certainly have one talent anyway, and perhaps God will help you to use that to His glory."

"I'm sure I haven't," said Barbara.

"You have forgotten your voice," answered Mother. "You know how beautifully you can sing when you want to. Perhaps—who knows?—you may be able to keep your promise by singing for Jesus."

"Me?" asked Barbara. "How could I? No one would listen to a little girl like me."

"I'm not so sure," said Mother. "You seem to have forgotten that it is nearly Christmas time, and people

56

will listen to children then, you know. That is, if they sing nicely and reverently."

"Do you mean that I could go out and sing carols at people's houses?"

"Well, not by yourself. But I've got an idea. There's Richard with his violin, and Bessie—she can sing too. I believe that the three of you might do wonderfully well. At any rate we could think about it."

A new light entered Barbara's eyes. Hope stirred anew within her little heart. That $2.50 she had promised seemed nearer than it had since she reached home.

All the next day they talked over Mother's idea, and in the evening the three children had a practice together, with Mother

at the piano. They soon found that they could get along very well with several simple hymns, and this made them full of eagerness to see what they could do outside.

Two evenings later they started out. And what a happy time they did have! Barbara sang as she had never sung at home. She felt she was using her one talent for Jesus. People opened their windows to listen to the clear, musical little voice that rang out on the still evening air. Richard played very well on his violin, and Bessie helped a lot too. She knocked at the doors and told the story of how they were all trying to gather money so that their missionary would not have to be brought back from India. No one could resist her sweet little smile. At every house she received something. One lady gave five cents, another ten cents, and one happy old gentleman brought a quarter out of his trousers pocket.

When at last they all reached home, they were so excited and happy that Mother scarcely knew what to do with them. After counting up their money, they found they had collected ninety-four cents.

"Why!" exclaimed Barbara, "we shall have to go out only three or four times to get more than I promised."

"It's wonderful," said Mother. "I prayed that God would bless you tonight, and I am sure He has. That one talent came in useful, didn't it, Barbara?"

Barbara blushed a little.

"Anyway," she said, "I'm glad I shall be able to keep my promise, and have something to give Him after all."

59

What a wonderful time they had! Barbara sang while Richard played his violin, and Bessie knocked at the doors and smiled sweetly.

Katie, Chris, and the Christmas Tree

It was the day before Christmas, and still there was no Christmas tree in its usual corner in the dining room.

Katie and Chris had crept into the room day after day, hoping to see it there as they had in years gone by, but the corner was always empty. They waited and waited, expecting to find it there any minute, only to be disappointed every time they looked.

Now it was the very last day. They felt they couldn't wait any longer. They just had to ask Mother about it, and so they did.

"Mamma," asked Chris, "aren't we going to have a Christmas tree this year?"

"This is Christmas Eve," added Katie.

Mother's face fell. She had dreaded this moment.

"Darlings, I'm so sorry," she said. "I'm afraid we won't have one this year. I asked Daddy to bring us one, but he has been so busy he forgot all about it. He told me so last night, and now it's too late. We live so far from town we never could get one in time.

60

"Oh, Mamma!" cried Chris. "We do love the pretty tree in the corner. It won't be the same without it."

"It's too bad," said Mamma. "I'll have to make it up to you some other way."

"But we want the tree," said Chris.

"Yes, we want the tree," echoed Katie.

The two children ran away to share their grief. But there was nothing anybody could do about it. At least, it seemed that way.

Then as they talked together, Katie said, "Chris, if we were to tell Jesus about the tree, do you think He would send us one?"

"Maybe He would," said Chris.

So, without telling Mother a word about it, they got down on their knees and told Jesus what was in their hearts, the thing they wanted most just then.

You may say, Fancy asking Jesus for a Christmas tree! I know. It does sound strange. But Jesus understands little children, and loves to have them tell Him all their hopes and dreams.

He likes to surprise them, too! I know He does.

That very evening, soon after Katie and Chris had gone to bed, there was a knock on the front door. Who should it be but the neighbor who lived on the farm next to theirs. He had a strange tale to tell.

Coming back from town that very evening, he said, he had been stopped by a stranger

61

and asked whether he would take something to the home of Katie and Chris.

"I looked at him carefully," said the neighbor, "and tried to think who he could be; but he was nobody I had seen before; and I have lived here all my life and know everyone for miles around."

"That's strange," said Mother. "But what did he give you to bring us?"

"That's the funny thing about it," said the neighbor. "He gave me a Christmas tree, of all things; and I'm sure you have one already."

"But we haven't!" cried Mother. "And the children want one so very much. Who could have sent it to us?"

"I don't know," said the neighbor, "but here it is, a very beautiful one, too."

At the words "Christmas tree," Katie and Chris—who had been listening hard all the time—came bounding out of bed to where Mother and the neighbor were standing at the front door.

And there was the tree, the biggest and most beautiful Christmas tree they had seen in all their lives.

"Oh!" they cried together. "What a perfectly lovely tree!"

62

"I knew Jesus would send it!" said Katie.

"I knew He would, too," said Chris.

And Katie told me herself—she and Chris are both grown up now—that all her life she has never forgotten that wonderful night or the thrill she felt as she realized that her prayer had been answered.

How Ginger Paid His Bill

Here is a delightful little dog story, told me by a friend the other day.

Arriving home late one evening with his wife, he turned on the light in the hall, and was about to go upstairs, when he stopped suddenly.

What was that?

Noises!

Their hearts almost stopped beating.

Fancy burglars coming to their home! What should they do?

Standing very still, they listened fearfully.

The noise continued. Strange! Surely a burglar would have heard the click of the door, or noticed the light go on—unless he had found something of unusual value.

My friend decided to explore, and very carefully, treading softly to avoid the creaks, he crept upstairs.

Ah! A bedroom door opened, and something dark and big sprang out.

It wasn't a burglar but a big brown retriever.

Looking further, my friend discovered that the dog had

64

gotten in through an unfastened window, and had actually slept on the bed for some time, probably having had his slumbers disturbed by the return of the owners.

Whose dog was he?

Well, it turned out that he had once lived in this house, and feeling lonely, no doubt, had come back to his old home.

Ginger, as they called him, was given some food, which he ate hungrily. Later, very politely, of course, he was shown the door.

But that was not the end of it.

In the morning what should they discover on the top of the stairs but a bag of small cakes!

Who put them there?

Only Ginger could have done it. Why? Who knows? Was it his strange, doggy way of saying, "Thank you," and paying for his sleep on the bed?

Who can tell? Who will ever know?

What I would like to know,

and what I'm sure you would like to know is, Where did Ginger get the cakes?

Perhaps that's not a fair question. His honesty and kindly thoughtfulness lead me to throw a veil of secrecy over what might possibly have been a rash misdeed.

After all, I thought to myself, does not the Bible tell us that love covers a multitude of sins?

When the Guards Saluted

I saw an unusual sight in Rome some time ago. It happened at the Tomb of the Unknown Warrior.

After the first world war, as your daddy has probably told you, each nation in the conflict took one of the dead men from the battlefield, someone so badly hurt that he could not be recognized, someone without a number or a name, and buried him with great honor, surpassing that given to princes and generals. This was to show that they were grateful for all the sufferings of the millions of poor, common, unknown people who had to do the fighting and the dying.

Probably you have seen the Tomb of the Unknown Soldier at Arlington, or in Westminster Abbey, or under the Arc de Triomphe in Paris, where a flame is kept constantly burning in his memory.

But it is about the one in Rome I want to tell you now. It is in the center of the city, and is part of a very beautiful and very massive, stately monument. Giant wreaths decorate the spot, and two soldiers, fully armed, stand on guard.

As I watched these two soldiers for a few minutes, I noticed

67

something very unusual. They saluted everybody who passed—men, women, and little children—all, in fact, who saluted the honored dead whose tomb they guarded.

Forward and backward went their rifles as people mounted the steps, saluted, and passed by. I was afraid they would get mixed up sometimes and fail to salute in unison—and they surely did; but in a moment they recovered themselves and continued their strangely beautiful task.

Naturally, I was particularly interested in the children who had come to honor the dead hero. Would the two stern guards recognize their salute also?

Yes. They did. And the children, who didn't understand very well, I think, what it all meant, seemed to enjoy it. Fancy being able to make a real, live soldier, with a big gun and a bayonet in his hand, salute you! The boys and girls all took full advantage of the opportunity. And as they walked, arms raised, before the sentries, up would go the guns, and the children would look *very* pleased with themselves.

Only one was disappointed. She was just a tiny little girl, about two and a half, I should say, dressed in a pretty pink frock, and she held up her hand again and again, but all in vain. Perhaps she was so very little that the guards did not see her. Anyhow, they didn't return her salute, and she went down the steps again with her daddy, feeling very sorry for herself.

68

I wondered what would happen if a foreigner went by; so I crossed in front and raised my arm like the others. (For though I hate war, I honor all men who suffer and die for some great ideal.) Up went the guns again, and I began to understand why the children liked to go by so often.

As I thought about it afterward, it seemed to me that those two soldiers were really doing what the poor dead man behind them would like to do could he see all the world coming to do him honor. They were responding on his behalf, and because he was just a poor, unknown man, one of the common people, they saluted everybody, poor and rich, young and old, friend and stranger.

I think that is how we should act also, don't you? We are to do what Somebody else would do if He were here. As Paul once said, "We are ambassadors for Christ"—we are "in Christ's stead."

So just as Jesus loved everybody and was kind to all, we too are to have the same friendly spirit. Not just talking to the boys and girls who have plenty of money, or who have some influential relatives, or who can do us some service in return, but being friendly and courteous to all, whoever they may be, whatever their name or station.

And, of course, unlike those two guards at the tomb, *we* must never overlook the tiniest of little ones, however small they be, who look up to us for help or guidance, or just a kindly greeting. For them especially, best beloved of Heaven, we must ever have a tender watchcare and a smile of love.

How John Saved His Daddy

After reading in *Bedtime Stories* about the wonderful way in which children's prayers have been answered, an old friend of mine sent me the following thrilling story:

With her husband and little son she lives in a very lonely section of New South Wales, Australia. Some distance from the tiny farmhouse runs a river which, usually calm and well-behaved, sometimes, after heavy rain, overflows its banks and does a lot of damage.

Well, it had been raining and raining for days, and little John was beginning to wonder whether the sun would ever shine again. Father, too, was very anxious, for he knew what so much rain might mean. All this time the river was rising nearer and nearer to the top of its banks. Would the rain stop before the water came over?

If Mother were only at home, thought John and his daddy. Somehow things always seemed brighter then; but she wasn't, having gone away to nurse a sick friend. So the two were all alone, waiting, watching, wondering, and hoping.

71

All of a sudden Daddy raised a cry.

"Look! It's over the top!"

It was. Though the surging flood was half a mile away, they could see it rushing toward them.

The cattle, the sheep, the chickens! what would happen to them as the waters surged by?

There was not a moment to lose.

"Stay on the veranda!" cried Father to John. "I'll be back in a minute."

And off he dashed in a desperate effort to reach the barns.

Crash! Splash! The water had reached the farmhouse and swept beyond it.

John stood on the veranda, breathless with excitement, and very much frightened.

Where was Daddy? What had happened to him?

Ah, there he was! He could see him now, with the water

up to his waist, and it was rising rapidly every moment.

But look! He was off his feet, floundering in the water, being fast swept away in the awful torrent, with cows and chickens and the driftwood from many barns and houses, smashed to pieces farther up the river.

John was helpless, terrified.

Then in that awful moment he remembered Jesus, and how Mother had taught him to pray "in every time of need."

Could Jesus help now?

"Jesus!" he cried frantically. "Jesus! Don't let Daddy drown! Please, please, don't let Daddy drown!"

He wrung his hands, and tears started to his eyes.

Then a strange thing happened. You may smile at it, but it is true.

At that very moment, when all seemed lost, a long-handled pitchfork, of all things, came floating toward the spot where

Daddy was fighting desperately for his life. Eagerly he grabbed it, and driving it deep into the ground, held on till the worst of the flood had passed. Then, making his way to a fence, the top of which was just sticking up above the water, he managed at last to find his way back home.

Was John glad to see him safe and sound? I should say so!

"Just an accident, a happen so," I can hear someone whisper.

Well, John doesn't think so, nor does his daddy or his mummy. They think it was just another evidence that "the angel of the Lord encampeth round about them that fear Him, and delivereth them" (Psalm 34:7), and that Jesus loves to hear little boys pray and to answer their prayers.

At the Dog Show

Have you ever been to a dog show? For years and years I wanted to go to one, and never seemed to find time just when the show was on. But not long ago I went to one, and what a lot of dogs I saw!

Big dogs and little dogs; pretty dogs and ugly dogs; white dogs and black dogs and brown dogs; dogs with long pointed noses; dogs with short stubby noses; dogs with long curly hair; dogs with short straight hair. I really had not imagined there could be so many different kinds of dogs in the world.

I could not help wondering about their owners. I suppose no matter how unattractive some of the dogs were to me, their owners were proud of them or they wouldn't have been there.

I was not there very long, but long enough to notice one very interesting thing.

It was this:

The dogs had been arranged in two main sections—big dogs on the ground floor and little dogs on the first floor upstairs.

What drew my attention first to this arrangement was the difference in the noise from both places.

75

Downstairs I could hear the occasional gruff, deep-toned barks and growls from bulldogs, Alsatians, retrievers, and the like. There was something very stolid, very stately, very important, about the sound from the big dogs.

Upstairs, however, it was altogether different. This was surely the noisiest place on earth. Every little dog was having his say, trying to shout louder than all the other little dogs around him.

Yap-yap, yap-yap, yap-yap, yap-yap, yap-yap-yap!

It was simply dreadful. There wasn't a moment's peace and quiet anywhere. They were all at it at once.

It made me wonder whether most boys and girls could not be divided—roughly, anyway—into two such groups.

Some are quiet, solid, and reliable, liking a bit of fun now and then, but going on with the job as soon as it is over. This kind of boy or girl thinks a great deal, but doesn't talk too much. He prefers reading a book to telling silly stories. He gives an occasional bark when it is needed, but has no time to "yap."

The others—well, who doesn't know them? They're in the majority, I'm afraid, just as there are far more little dogs than big dogs.

And, oh, how they yap! You hear them on the train, on the streetcar, on the tennis court, or the baseball diamond—everywhere you go.

Yap-yap, yap-yap, yap-yap! Isn't it tiresome?

They are the sort that quarrel about whether a boy is to be pitcher or catcher, or whether another made a run or was touched out, or whether the ball was fair or foul.

Or, if they are girls, they talk themselves tired about movie stars, or the latest fashion in dresses, or the new girl's style of hairdressing.

Oh, I know many such boys and girls, and so do you.

Big dog or little dog, which would you like to be? Do you belong upstairs or down? Not all the dogs at the show were prize winners, but nothing need stop you from being a prize winner.

Faithful Jock

T alking about dogs reminds me of one I saw this summer in a most unexpected place. I'll call him Jock, for, though I tried hard, I never found out his real name, but it really doesn't matter.

I was traveling over that long, long trail from the Pacific Coast to Chicago. The train was climbing the western slopes of the Rocky Mountains at the time, round and round, twist and turn, up and up, many thousand feet above the sea.

One mighty desolation it is, with an awful grandeur of its own. For miles and miles the train hurtles on with never a sign of human habitation, unless perhaps a tiny shack of a lonely rancher, or a group of railway workers beside the track.

No man's land it is in very truth.

And then—a dog!

I could hardly believe my eyes, and leaned out of the window to make sure. Yes, there he was, a fine black retriever, running at top speed beside the train!

Where did he live? Why was he there? Did he want the train to stop and take him on board?

79

Every day faithful Jock ran beside the train, then stopped and dashed after the newspaper that was thrown out to him from the last coach.

Then an interesting thing happened. From the very last coach a newspaper was thrown out by somebody. Instantly the dog stopped, turned, and dashed after it, as though eager to learn the latest news of the outside world.

A porter came to the window where I was standing, and as we watched the fast-receding form of the dog, I asked whether he knew anything about him.

"Yes," said the porter, "that is the most faithful dog I have ever known. He belongs to a man who lives in that little hut over yonder, and for years now, winter and summer, he has met this train to pick up his master's paper. Winter or summer, he never fails, and we expect him here as regularly as the sunrise."

"But how about the winter snows, when you have to run a snowplow in front of the train?" I asked.

"It makes no difference to him. Snow or rain or hail, he is always here on time. In fact, if he weren't, we'd wonder what had happened."

Faithful Jock! Bless his dear old courageous heart!

Do you wonder that I leaned out of the window once more to catch one last glimpse of his shining black coat as he disappeared down the bank in the gloaming?

Geoffrey's Bandsmen

It happened on the way back from a band concert. I mean the quarrel happened then.

As a special treat, Geoffrey and his sister Anne had been taken to hear the band one evening.

They loved going to the band, and would promise their daddy that they would be good as angels for weeks if only he would take them there.

Of course, as soon as the music was over they usually forgot all about their promises.

Well, the band was over one night, and Daddy, Geoffrey, and Anne had started to walk home. Unfortunately, both children wanted to hold Daddy's right hand. A very silly thing, of course, for surely Daddy's left hand was just as comfortable to hold as his right hand. But then most quarrels start over very silly little things.

"I was there first," said Geoffrey.

"No, you weren't; I was," said Anne.

"I was; you get away," said Geoffrey.

"I was; you get away," retorted Anne.

"What does it matter?" asked Daddy.

"I had your right hand first," said Geoffrey.

"No; I did," said Anne. "Anyway, it's my turn."

"No, it isn't."

"It is."

"It isn't."

"Stop it, children!" cried Daddy. "What will people think of you both, making all this fuss at this time of night?"

"It's my place," said Geoffrey, taking no notice, and trying still harder to push Anne away.

"It isn't yours; it's mine," cried Anne, holding on to Daddy's hand still more tightly.

"Will you stop it, Geoffrey?" said Daddy firmly. "Come round and take my other hand at once."

"Don't want to," said Geoffrey sulkily, suddenly dropping behind. "I'll walk by myself then."

"All right," replied Daddy. "But next band night things will be different."

So the procession moved toward home, with Geoffrey dropping farther and farther behind, and shuffling his feet along in a manner that must have made the angels weep.

It was long past bedtime when they reached home. Mamma hurried the children up to bed without making too many inquiries as to what had happened.

Geoffrey was soon between the sheets, and it was not long before he dropped off into a troubled slumber.

Hello! What was this? He was at the band again. Surely it could not be! But he was. And to his utter amazement, he was the conductor. Behind him were hundreds of people, many of whom he recognized. Lots of boys from his school were there too. He felt very proud of himself. Fancy being the conductor of the band in front of all his school friends. My! wouldn't they all like to be in his shoes? He made up his mind that he would make their ears tingle with the wonderful music he would bring from the band that night.

Then he looked around at his bandsmen. Yes, they were all there. Were they ready to play? Yes. He tapped his baton smartly on the music holder, and swelled up with pride. But nobody moved.

He tapped again. No one seemed to take the least notice.

"Start!" he shouted. "Can't you hear me? Start!"

At this the drummer banged his drum and the man with the trombone blew one great long note. The people behind him laughed. He could hear his school friends tittering.

"Play!" he cried again. "Start! All of you start!"

He tapped furiously on the music holder.

The man with the piccolo blew a piercing blast and stopped. Then the cornets began, but they all seemed to be playing different tunes. Geoffrey was in despair. He waved his arms in an endeavor to beat time, but there was no time. Rather, there were all sorts of time. The clarinets had begun now, all on different notes. Geoffrey shouted to them to look at their music, but they took no notice. Now all the rest of the players began, and the confusion became terrible. It seemed as if each one were playing a tune of his own. No one took any notice of anybody but himself. Geoffrey could hear "Three Blind Mice" and "Home Sweet Home" and "Old Man River" all mixed up

together. Every man was playing just what he liked and how he liked and in any time he liked.

As for Geoffrey, the players took no notice of him whatever. He might as well not have been there. And yet he felt that he was responsible. The people behind him were expecting great things of him. And this was all he could do! It was terrible. As the din increased, Geoffrey became frantic.

"Stop!" he shrieked at them all. "Stop! Stop it, I say! Can't you hear me? Do what you're told, will you! Oh, why don't you listen to me? Stop! Stop, I say! Stop!"

"There, there," said Mamma, putting her hand on his head. "It's all right, dear; don't worry any more."

Geoffrey sat bolt upright in bed.

"So I'm not at the band, after all," he said.

"At the band?" laughed Daddy. "You're right here in bed."

"Oh!" said Geoffrey. "You should have heard them. They just wouldn't do what I told them, Daddy. They were so obstinate. They just played their own tunes as loud as they could, and wouldn't take a bit of notice when I shouted at them."

"Who?" asked Daddy.

"The bandsmen, of course. Didn't you hear the noise?"

"Well, no, I can't say that I did," said Daddy. "I heard a noise, and I also saw someone acting like that on the way back from the band tonight."

"Oh—er—yes," said Geoffrey, waking up fully at last. "I wonder if that's why I dreamed that dreadful dream."

"I should think it was," said Daddy.

"Well, of all things," said Geoffrey as he dropped back on his pillow and went to sleep.

Geoffrey's dream was not forgotten in the morning, and Daddy found it very useful later on when the old trouble began to come back again.

For whenever Geoffrey showed any signs of grumpiness or disobedience after that, all Daddy had to say was, "How about your bandsmen, Geoffrey?"

It always had a wonderful effect!

Grandma's Piano

Ruth loved to stay at her grandma's house, for she always had a happy time there. Grandma was kind and good to her, telling her stories, mending her dolly's clothes, and of course, giving her nice things to eat.

Every Wednesday night Grandma would put Ruth to bed early, then walk across town to Mrs. Henderson's house to attend prayer meeting. Except for illness or a very bad storm, Grandma had not missed a prayer meeting in twenty years. Even now that she was "getting on in years," as she said, she was determined to be there, come what might.

One day, while Ruth and Grandma were having a little chat together, Ruth asked a question which seemed to puzzle the old lady quite a bit.

"Grandma," asked Ruth, "why do you have to go all the way to Mrs. Henderson's house for the prayer meeting? It's too far for you to walk nowadays."

"Well, darling," said Grandma, "I don't think I have ever thought about it. We've all been going to Mrs. Henderson's house for years and years, and I suppose I shall keep on going

87

there as long as I live."

"But, Grandma," persisted Ruth, "why don't you have the prayer meeting in your house? Then you wouldn't have to walk anywhere!"

"I suppose I never stopped to think about it," said Grandma, smiling. "Oh, yes, I did. I know. It's because I don't have a piano and Mrs. Henderson does. So there you are, dear, that's the reason."

But if Grandma thought that Ruth would be satisfied with that, she was mistaken.

"Grandma," said the little girl after a while, "why don't you have a piano in your house?"

"Because," said Grandma, "I don't really need a piano. I could still play it, though, if I had one."

"But, Grandma," said Ruth, "you really do need one; then you wouldn't have to go out in the cold and wet; and you wouldn't have to walk so far."

"I know, darling," said Grandma, "but there's another reason—and a very important one, too. I couldn't afford to buy a piano if I wanted one. I think we had better leave things just as they are."

88

"But, Grandma," said Ruth, "couldn't Jesus give you a piano?"

"Of course He could," said Grandma; "but I don't think He will because—well, as I told you, I don't really need one."

"But, Grandma, you do need one," said Ruth, "and I am going to ask Jesus to send you one. Won't it be lovely when you have a piano of your very own, and the people all come here to the prayer meeting?"

Grandma smiled and sighed. She did not know what to say now. Not for a million dollars would she destroy Ruth's faith in the power and love of Jesus.

"Well, dear," she said finally, "we must leave it all to Him, mustn't we?"

"Oh, yes, Grandma," said Ruth. "Of course we must, but I am going to ask Him to send you one."

And faithful little Ruth kept her promise.

Morning by morning, evening by evening, she sent up the sweet and loving petition, "Please, Jesus, send Grandma a piano, so she won't have to go so far to the prayer meeting."

I don't know exactly how long it was before the answer came —maybe two or three weeks, maybe a month. Then one afternoon, as Grandma and Ruth were sitting together in the dining room and Grandma was putting a stitch or two in Ruth's dolly, they were suddenly aroused by strange sounds outside the door.

Some men were shouting to each other.

"Heave ho!" cried one. "Steady there," cried another. "Steady now. Take it easy, men. Take it easy."

Then the men seemed to be climbing the stairs to the front door, coming ever closer and closer. Grandma stopped her work and looked up.

"What is that?" she asked. "Who can be coming to see us this afternoon?"

"Steady now," came the voices again. "Take it easy. Let her down carefully. Don't let her fall. Careful now, careful."

Then there was a loud bang on the front door.

Ruth's eyes sparkled with excitement.

"Grandma!" she cried. "Perhaps it's your piano. Oh, Grandma, I know it is—let's go and see!"

Ruth flew across the room and opened the door.

"Grandma! It is! Jesus has sent your piano."

90

"I don't know who sent it," said one of the men; "but here it is, and what are we to do with it?"

"Bring it in; bring it in!" said Ruth, while Grandma stood back wondering what all this might mean, but with a little prayer of thankfulness in her heart, both for the gift and the faith of her little granddaughter.

They found out afterward that the piano had belonged to one of the prayer-meeting ladies who was leaving town and who, not knowing what to do with it, had suddenly had the idea of sending it to Grandma.

So here it was at last! A real piano! Right in Grandma's own house! No matter who sent it, or why, Ruth was absolutely sure that it had come in answer to her prayer. Grandma said she believed it had, too.

Kidnaped!

Have you ever wondered what it would be like to be kidnaped? Perhaps you have asked yourself just what you would do if a stranger suddenly picked you up and hurried you away in his car. Well, here is the story of a little boy who had this experience. I know it is true, for his mother wrote and told me all about it.

I am going to call him Raymond, for, of course, he wouldn't want me to use his real name.

He was just six years old at the time this happened, but though he was very young, he loved to do what he called his "missionary work." That is, when the minister at his church said that he needed money to send to the missionaries in foreign lands, Raymond would set out bravely to call at the neighbors' homes and tell them all about it. It was really surprising how much money he would bring home sometimes.

One day, in the summer of 1942, Raymond had been out collecting his "missionary money." He was almost finished. As he was walking home along a country road he suddenly heard a car slow down and stop beside him. A strange man put his head

92

out of the window and asked Raymond if he wanted a ride.

"No, thank you," said Raymond, remembering his mother's strict warning that he was never to accept a ride from a stranger.

"Oh, come on," said the man.

"Thank you; I'd rather walk," said Raymond. "I do not have very far to go."

The stranger opened the door and got out.

"Get in there," he ordered, picking Raymond up bodily and shoving him on the front seat.

"But I don't want to ride!" shouted Raymond. "Let me out!"

It was no use. Already the door was shut and the man was

starting the car. Soon they were moving rapidly along the road.

"What's your name?" asked the stranger.

"Raymond."

"Who's your father?"

Raymond told him.

"How much money does he earn?"

"Don't know," said Raymond. And at the mention of money he became more frightened, for he remembered the "missionary money" in his pocket which he had gathered that very afternoon. He hoped this bad man would not find out about it.

Now the car was speeding past his home, and Raymond saw all the old familiar places being left behind.

"Oh, dear!" he thought, "where is he going to take me?"

Then he remembered that Mother had said that if he was working for Jesus, he need never be afraid, for the angels would surely look after him. So he began to say a little prayer; but he was so frightened that he said it out loud.

"What was that you were saying?" asked the man.

"I was asking Jesus to save me," said Raymond, as the tears rolled down his cheeks.

"Oh, very well, then, very well," said the man, putting his foot on the brake. "Get out; get out!"

With that he stopped the car, opened the door, and pushed

Raymond onto the grass at the side of the road. Then he jumped in again, and the car roared away into the distance.

As Raymond stood there wondering what to do next, a woman from a nearby farm came up to him and asked, "What in the world are you doing all alone out here?"

Raymond told her all that had happened. Getting her own car, she drove him back to his mother.

Mother said he was a very brave boy, but Raymond said he was quite sure all the time that Jesus would help him because of the "missionary money" he had in his pocket that afternoon.

I think He did too; don't you?

In the Mirror

Have you ever noticed that when you look in a mirror, your hands—if you are a boy—instinctively go to your tie, to pull it straight?

If you're a girl, they probably go to your hair, to pat it into shape, you know.

I suppose that's because we really do want to look as neat and tidy as possible, and the mirror shows us what's out of place.

It doesn't have to be a glass mirror, either. A very calm lake will do just as well. Maybe you have seen one. There is a much-advertised Mirror Lake in California, and it certainly is pretty, the mountains and trees being perfectly reflected in the water. But there are many others. Long ago I saw one in the highlands of Scotland, and the reflection was wonderful.

There are other kinds of mirrors, too.

Perhaps you are the proud possessor of a watch. If you are, then next time you pass a very big clock that you are sure always has the right time, notice what you do.

Of course, you will look at your watch and compare it with the great big clock, and if they don't agree, you will turn the hands of your watch until they do. That's like looking in a mirror, isn't it? Only you put the watch's tie straight instead of your own.

Then there is another kind of mirror—the law of God. So the Bible says. (James 1:23-25.) But how can the Ten Commandments be a mirror?

You do something that is questionable, something that you feel is wrong, but you are not quite sure. Then you look at the Ten Commandments, that wonderful, divine mirror; and conscience tells you at once that there is something out of place—something about you that needs to be put straight.

And put it straight you must, though you cannot do that yourself. As soon as you see that there is something wrong with you, then you must ask the dear Lord Jesus to help you make it right.

That may mean begging somebody's pardon for saying rude things, or giving back something you have taken that does not belong to you, or correcting a false story you have thoughtlessly passed on. Whatever it is, He will help you do it, for, as the Good Book says, "If we confess our sins, He is faithful and just to forgive us our sins, and to cleanse us from all unrighteousness." 1 John 1:9.

Then you will be able to look in the mirror again and see that all is well—until the next time.

Ah, that is the worst of it. There is always a next time; we keep having to go back to the mirror, don't we? But one day, by the grace of God, we shall have become so like Jesus that to look in His mirror will bring us no regrets.

Then, too, we shall be mirrors also, for He, looking at us, will see a perfect reflection of Himself!

How wonderful!

May that happy day soon dawn for us all.

PAINTING BY RUSSELL HARLAN

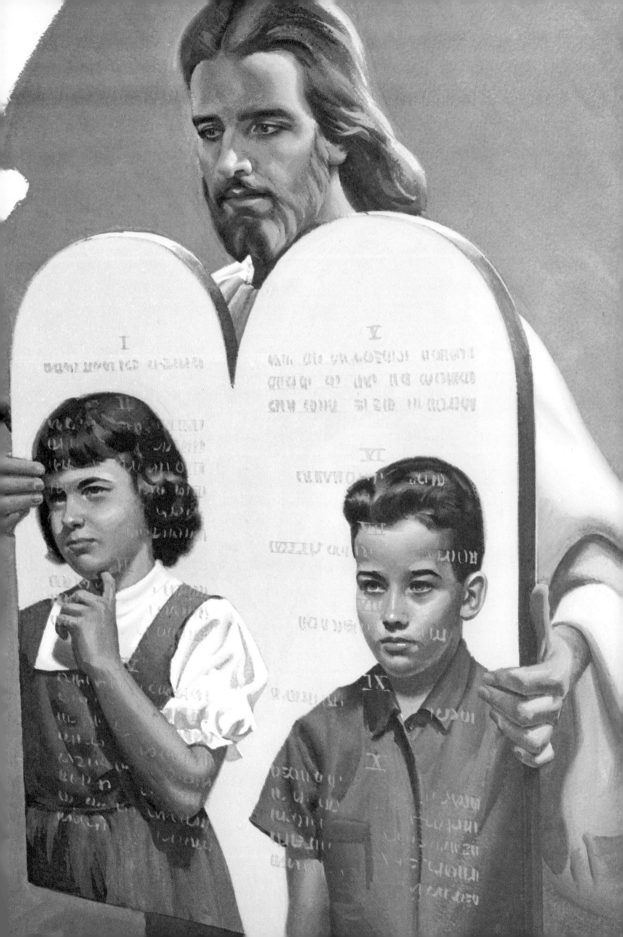

Muriel's Customer

Little Muriel was a very lonely girl. Her mother had been taken ill and sent to a hospital, and she had come to stay with her auntie.

She liked being with her auntie all right, but there was no one to play with. Auntie was getting old and seemed to have forgotten that she had ever been a child herself. Muriel was sure she didn't understand little girls. She was always saying, "Please be quiet, Muriel," and "Don't get into mischief, Muriel," until poor Muriel didn't know just what to do to be good.

One day Auntie got an idea. "When I was a little girl," she said, "we used to play store."

"I'd like to play store," said Muriel, glad to find something at last that Auntie thought was "being good," and happy to find a new interest.

So Auntie allowed Muriel to take some wooden boxes out into the garden, also some old cans that had once contained candy and cookies.

For a little while Muriel was very happy arranging the coun-

100

ter, but when that was done, she began to be lonesome again, for what is the good of a store if there is no one to buy your goods?

So she got one of her old dolls, propped it up in front of the counter, and pretended that it was a customer. But a doll is a very poor sort of customer. For one thing it will not take the things away, and for another it will not pay for them. So poor Muriel soon got tired of that, and told the doll to go away.

"Oh, dear!" she sighed. "I do wish someone would come to play with me!"

Hardly had she spoken when a nice tabby cat walked slowly

around the corner of the store, and jumped up on a box in front of the counter.

"Well, you are a nice customer!" said Muriel, smiling for the first time that afternoon. "And what would you like to buy today, Mr. Pussycat?"

"A penny's worth of sugar," said Mr. Pussycat as well as he could, opening his mouth wide and getting rather too near the sugar bag for safety.

Muriel guessed what he meant, and held up a piece of sugar to see if she had guessed rightly.

Mr. Pussycat opened his mouth wider still and swallowed the lump of sugar with relish. Evidently Muriel had not been mistaken.

"But now, Mr. Pussycat, how about paying for it?" said Muriel sternly. "Nobody is allowed to take things from this store without paying for them, you know."

Mr. Pussycat raised his right foot as if about to pass over the right amount of money, and Muriel took the will for the deed.

Well, they had great times together. So long as the supply of sugar lasted, Mr. Pussycat was a regular customer, and Muriel succeeded in selling him quite a number of other things as well. He came back the next day, and they started all over again.

Muriel got a bright idea, and decided to enlarge her store and add a dairy. Mr. Pussycat strongly approved, and came back frequently to purchase saucerfuls of milk. The only trouble was to get Auntie to understand why so much milk was needed in the store.

In a very little while Muriel and Mr. Pussycat became great friends. He would follow her about everywhere she went, and even when Auntie took her out shopping Mr. Pussycat would

103

follow behind like a little dog. They played together all day long, and in her love for her pussy Muriel forgot her loneliness.

Then one day a letter came saying that Mother was better and Muriel could go home again. She didn't know whether to laugh for joy at the thought of going home or cry for sadness at parting from her new-found friend.

So she played one last game of store and sold Mr. Pussycat

all the milk he could drink and all the sugar he could eat, and didn't charge him anything for it either. Then she said good-by with tears running down her cheeks.

Auntie said it was very foolish for a little girl to cry over a cat, especially when she ought to be so thankful that her mother was better, but Muriel just couldn't help it.

Soon she was home again, and so glad to see Mamma well and strong once more. But somehow she couldn't forget her friend, and longed to have him with her always.

Then one morning, what do you suppose happened?

Well, it was her birthday, and when she went into the dining room she saw a large parcel beside her plate on the breakfast table. Quickly she removed the paper. Underneath was a basket, and in the basket was—Mr. Pussycat.

So Auntie had understood after all!

The Treasure Hunt

It had been a dreary, wet afternoon, with the rain coming down in bucketfuls. And from the way it was still coming down, the children thought it would go on raining forever and ever.

Everybody was about as miserable as he could be, and a bit short-tempered, too, if the truth must be told.

The children had played every game they could think of, and now there just didn't seem to be anything else to do.

It was when things were getting as gloomy inside as they were outside that Mother came along with one of her bright ideas.

"I'll tell you what," she said cheerfully, "let's have a treasure hunt."

There was a chorus of approval.

"Good idea!" shouted Wilfred. "What shall we hunt?"

"Will there be a prize?" cried Sylvia.

"Anything for a change," gasped Gilbert from his seat on the sofa. "Let's start."

"I want to hunt, too," cried Baby. "Let me hunt, Mamma."

106

"All in good time," said Mother. "Now listen. I have buried a treasure somewhere in this house, and I'm going to give you fifteen minutes to find it. The one who finds it will win the cake I've bought for supper."

"Good!" said Wilfred. "I'm going to find it then."

"But what is it like?" asked Sylvia. "We don't know anything about it yet."

"Well," said Mother mysteriously, "it's not very small and it's not very big."

"But that's not enough. We might bring anything," said Gilbert.

"I know," Mother went on. "But this particular object is the most valuable thing in the house, and you have to think what this is before you begin to look."

"Um," said Wilfred frowning. "What can it be? I didn't think there was anything very valuable in this house. Is it the old grandfather clock?"

"No!" said Mother, "of course not, and please don't try to bring that in here. And I'll tell you this: It's more than an inch square and less than a foot square.

It is not locked, but when you open it, you will find lots of valuable things inside."

"Oh, I can't imagine what it is!" exclaimed Gilbert, lazily.

"Think, then," said Mother. "I'm going to start counting in just a minute from now. And mind, if you look in any cupboards or drawers, you must leave everything exactly as you find it. If you don't, you'll lose the prize anyway. Now away you all go. One, two, thrrreeeee!"

Away they went.

Gilbert hurried to the cupboard where he remembered Father kept the little black box with some precious papers inside. But it was locked, so he went off on another scent.

Wilfred hunted upstairs, crawling under all the beds, with Baby at his heels, enjoying the fun immensely.

Bang! bang! bang! went the cupboard doors as one by one they were opened and closed.

Sylvia wandered about quietly with a thoughtful look on her face.

"Now, what can it be?" she said to herself. "The most valuable thing in the house? Um. It can't be money, for there isn't much of that. And it can't be jewelry, for Mother hasn't any. Um. It might be a picture, but it isn't more than a foot square, and we haven't any pictures that size. Um. It might be one of those queer curios on the mantelpiece in the parlor, but hardly so, for it is something that can be opened. Yes, opened. What things can be opened? Boxes and bags and brief cases, and, um, yes, books!"

Why, there was an idea. Why hadn't she thought of that before?

It might be one of the old books in the bookcase. She hurried over to it.

"Three more minutes!" called Mother from the kitchen.

"I've got something," cried Gilbert.

"So have I," shouted Wilfred, his voice seeming to come from the attic.

"And so have I," echoed Baby from the same quarter.

Feverishly Sylvia looked along the rows of books, but which one to choose she could not tell. Many of the titles she did not even recognize. There were books on history, astronomy, literature, and all sorts of things, with here and there a big fat dictionary. Suddenly, just between two of these large volumes she spied a smaller one, and a happy smile spread across her face.

109

"Got it!" she said to herself, as she picked it out and hurried with it to the dining room.

"Time!" called Mother.

Down came the others helter-skelter.

"Well, what have you found for me?" asked Mother.

"Your purse," said Gilbert.

"Ha, ha, ha!" laughed Mother. "So you think that's the most valuable thing in this house! Well, it isn't, by a long, long way, especially at the end of the week."

"I think I've got it," said Wilfred, bringing forth a dusty, old-fashioned mother-of-pearl workbox he had found in the attic.

"Well, I never did!" exclaimed Mother. "How did you find that? I haven't seen it for years and years. It belonged to my grandmother, and it is very precious to me; yet it isn't the most valuable thing that I hid specially and wanted you to find."

Wilfred looked rather disappointed.

"And what did you bring, Baby dear?" asked Mother.

110

"Just me," said Baby, at which, of course, Mother had to pick him up and hug him for a full minute.

"You surely are the sweetest thing," she said, kissing him. "But has nobody found what I hid?"

Sylvia was blushing a little, for she felt sure she had discovered the treasure, and at this moment produced her find.

"Well done!" cried Mother. "Sylvia has won! What made you think of it?"

"I don't know," said Sylvia. "I just saw it and guessed."

"Who'd have thought of that!" exclaimed Gilbert. "A Bible!"

"Yes," said Mother. "And I wonder you didn't all think of it together. Of course it's the most valuable thing in this house. When you open it you find it is full of the richest treasure. It is a gold mine of truth, full of beautiful stories of Jesus and His love. There is wonderful counsel here to keep us from making mistakes, from doing things we might be sorry for, and to tell us how to share at last in all the riches and glory of God's eternal kingdom. Why, there's nothing more precious."

"But you can buy it for a dollar," said Gilbert.

"I know," said Mother. "But remember, when one of the early copies of this Book was found some years ago, it took five hundred thousand dollars to buy it. Why, Gilbert, there isn't another book in the world for which people would give five hundred thousand dollars. The nearest to that was seventy-seven thousand dollars, paid for the original manuscript of *Alice in Wonderland*. Nobody would give *five hundred* thousand dollars for that or any other book. Only the Bible could bring such a price. Truly, the art of printing has made it cheap for us to buy, but it is just as precious inside as it ever was.

"Wish I'd thought of that," said Wilfred, looking woefully at the supper table.

"Never mind," said Sylvia gracefully, "I'll cut that cake into five pieces and share it with everybody."

Saved by an Onion

In the early days of American history, when the Western States were being developed, some of the hardest-working people were ministers of the gospel. These were the circuit riders, who rode on horseback from one community to another, preaching and conducting baptisms, marriages, and funerals. Sometimes they would be away from home for months at a time, enduring all sorts of hardships and riding thousands of miles a year.

Mr. Matthews was one of these brave and busy circuit riders. He had a huge parish, covering hundreds of miles in every direction, which constantly called for all his time and attention. With these heavy duties and his large family of twelve children, he was sometimes a very tired man.

Coming home one day after a long absence, he found that his son Jack had failed to complete some work that he had been told to do. Heated words were spoken, and it was not long before Jack was suffering from the effects of a severe spanking. Father simply would not put up with disobedience.

Now Jack was a high-spirited boy, and nothing wounded

his pride so much as being spanked, especially when he felt that he did not deserve it. This time he was so angry that he decided to run away.

His favorite sister, Elsie, who was about his own age, pleaded with him not to go, but he would not listen to her. She begged him to let everything rest for a few days, but nothing moved him. He was determined to go.

Next morning, without saying good-by to anyone but Elsie, Jack went away, determined never to return to his father's house.

Now it was Elsie's turn to be cross. She, of course, sided with Jack, and said it was her father's fault that he had gone away. Therefore she would have nothing to do with her father, or with his religion.

Every day she became more and more bitter. She would hardly speak to either of her parents and positively refused to take any part in family worship. She would neither read the Bible nor say her prayers, and in her heart she secretly resolved that she would never be a Christian, never!

Meanwhile no word came back from Jack. He had vanished completely out of the home. Elsie felt that the joy of life had gone away with him, and her heart became hard as steel.

Then one morning, while preparing the dinner, Mother discovered that she needed just one more onion, and Elsie was the only daughter near at hand to send.

"Elsie!" called Mother. "I do so need just one more onion to finish this potpie. I wish you would go and get me one."

"Where are they?" asked Elsie coldly.

"In the barn, on the second floor," said Mother. "Mind how you go up the ladder, dear. And you might as well bring me two or three extra ones while you are about it."

Elsie went without a word, or even a smile. She had long since ceased to smile around the house, and was secretly longing for the day when she, too, could run away. Then she would go and find Jack.

Going over to the barn, she climbed the ladder to the second floor, and, looking around, soon saw where the onions had been laid out for winter use. She picked up half a dozen, and was walking back to the ladder, when she heard a noise below.

Footsteps! Someone was coming stealthily toward the ladder.

Who could it be?

Holding her breath, she listened and guessed that it must be her father, the very last person on

earth she wished to meet at that particular moment. Suddenly all the hatred she had been fostering in her heart
overflowed. She did not want to speak to him, no, nor to look
at him. She never would again, never!

But what could she do?

Looking around quickly, she spied an old, unused door

leaning against the wall. It was the only possible shelter; so on tiptoe she ran swiftly toward it, and was barely hidden when she heard her father coming up the last section of the ladder.

Holding her breath for fear he would find her, she waited anxiously, hoping he would go down again immediately when he found the loft empty. But he did not go down. Instead Elsie heard a strange sound as of something falling gently on the floor, and she held her hands together in fright.

After a few moments of suspense she heard her father talking out loud. Had two people come up into the loft? No. He was praying!

Cramped behind that door, Elsie listened to the most wonderful prayer she had ever heard; and she couldn't run away from it. She just had to stay and hear every word.

Father was praying for his family. For every child, from the oldest to the youngest, for Elsie herself, and especially for Jack. When he reached Jack he broke down completely, sobbing as if his heart would break; asking God to forgive him for being so angry with Jack as to drive him away from home; praying that even now God would move upon Jack's heart by His Spirit and bring him back.

117

Elsie was stunned. She could hardly believe her ears.

So Father did love Jack after all! And wanted him home again! And was so very, very sorry he had been angry with him!

More than that, he was willing to pray for Elsie, too! Elsie, who had been so rude to him, so cruel to him all these many weeks since Jack had left. She knew she had not prayed for Father like that.

Suddenly she felt she could not stand it a moment longer. She must run from the scene, or her heart would break.

Elsie rose and slipped from behind the door. As she did so, she caught sight of Father kneeling on the floor, wiping the tears from his eyes.

She gave in.

"Father, I'm sorry," she said, putting her arms around his neck and bursting into tears.

"So are we all, Elsie," he said. And everything was all right again from that moment.

Meanwhile, Mother was beginning to fuss about the missing onion, wondering why Elsie had been so long getting it. But when she saw Father and daughter coming across the yard with arms around each other, faces tear-stained but radiant, she suddenly understood, and ran out to meet them, the onion and the pie all forgotten.

That night, believe it or not, Jack returned.

(In later years, by the way, Jack himself became a minister, and Elsie a minister's wife.)

Wonders of Today

In olden days it used to be said that there were just seven "wonders of the world," and they included such things as the pyramids of Egypt, the "hanging gardens" of Babylon, and some of the other great works of man that have long since been forgotten.

What are the seven wonders of the world today? What would you say? Why not take time one day to make a list of all the wonderful things you have seen, or heard about, and then try to pick out the seven greatest of them all.

I suppose you would start off with television, a truly marvelous invention that is still beyond the understanding of most of us. Indeed, if the ancients could have seen a picture sent hundreds

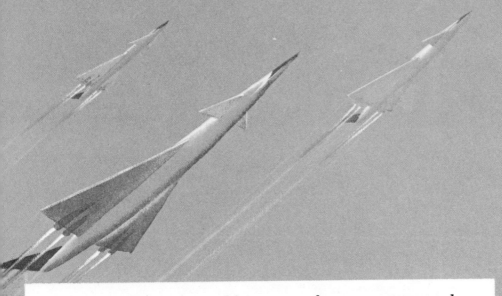

of miles without any visible means of communication, they would either have cried out, "Witchcraft!" or have fallen down in worship before it.

Early on your list you would no doubt have jet airplanes, helicopters, rocket ships, and space capsules.

Then you might think of the mighty bridges that men have thrown across great chasms, rivers and bays, gigantic structures that almost take your breath away as you look up at them, such as the seven-mile Chesapeake Bay Bridge and those over the Golden Gate and San Francisco Bay in California. Then there is the Forth Bridge in Scotland, the Sydney Bridge in Australia, the Zambesi Bridge over the Victoria Falls in Africa, and similar structures in many lands.

There are the great tunnels also, miles long, blasted through

the solid rock of the Alps. I passed though the Simplon Tunnel some years ago, and it took nearly fifteen minutes to do so. I timed it.

What would not the Caesars have paid for a tunnel through the Alps! Certainly they would never have believed it possible that one could be made. The Romans built some wonderful roads in their day, too, but what would they have thought of the beautiful Columbia River Highway, or the 4,000-mile-long Trans-Canada Highway, or the two-hundred-mile Pennsylvania Turnpike with not a single crossroad on it?

Then there are all the great ships that plow the oceans, each one containing a thousand marvels that would have made the men of olden days gasp with astonishment. Imagine Columbus being taken for a walk through the docks of New York Harbor, and staring up open-mouthed at the *America,* the *Queen Mary,* the *Queen Elizabeth,* and half a dozen other great ocean liners. Do you think you could ever make them realize that these mountains of steel could be driven through the water five times faster than a Spanish galley at full speed?

Should you go to a naval dockyard, you might see the battleships *North Carolina* or *New Mexico* or the aircraft carrier *Forrestal,* all giant floating fortresses crammed with the most marvelous inventions. Near them you would see atomic submarines—strange steel craft that can stay under water for weeks.

Yet you have only begun. A walk around any large department store, yes, even Woolworth's, will give you a hundred suggestions of new wonders to record. Think of the beautiful fabrics that are produced so cheaply today, and of the intricate machines that make them.

122

There is the modern newspaper, too, not much to be admired for its contents, perhaps, but when you think of its origin in the great forests, and of all the work that goes into the making of it, surely it is one of the greatest marvels of the age.

There is also the Palomar telescope in California, which enables astronomers to see twice as far into space as they ever saw before, and the giant radar receiver at Jodrell Bank in England, which listens to sounds coming from millions of miles away.

Having listed all these inventions, and many others besides, the record will still be by no means complete.

There are, in addition, great natural wonders such as Niagara Falls on the United States-Canadian border, Monument Valley in Utah, and the Painted Desert of Arizona.

North America possesses an unusual number of these wonders, such as the Grand Canyon of the Colorado, a vast chasm, hundreds of feet deep, and many miles in length, washed out by water action long centuries ago. It has also the famous Carlsbad Caverns in New Mexico, largest in the world, where, far beneath the surface of the earth, rock formations of great size blend in pictures of enchanting beauty.

Then there are the giant sequoia trees of California. Forests of these massive trees are still to be found there. Some of the largest are more than three hundred feet high and have a diameter, at their base, of thirty feet and more. If you will look at the picture illustrating this story, you will realize how very big they are. Fancy being able to drive a car right through the trunk of a tree!

These trees are among the oldest living things on the earth. Scores of them are over one thousand years old, some are two thousand, and a few, it is said, are at least three thousand. If so, it means that when Jesus was born in Bethlehem, these hoary old giants had already been growing for a thousand years, and they have lived through all the history of the world since then. What stories they could tell if only they could speak!

Even older are the bristlecone pines in the White Mountains of California, discovered in 1862, some of which are over 4,000 years old. These and some of the sequoias were alive in Solomon's day, and when great Pharaohs sat on the throne of Egypt. Babylon had not been thought of when their first shoots

124

Automobiles drive through the Wawona tree, one of the giant redwoods of Yosemite National Park.

rose above the earth. When Rome was but a village, their branches towered into the skies.

What man could make a living thing like this?

True, men made the pyramids, and they stand as they did many thousands of years ago, save where they have fallen into decay or been damaged by vandals; but the big trees have lived and gone on growing all this long, long time. This is the work of God.

And if we are looking for wonders, there are the stars above us, or the tiny blades of grass under our feet. There is the daily miracle of the tides, and of the sand on the seashore, which acts as a barrier that the sea may not pass over it. There is the miracle of the birds, how they sing so sweetly and how they fly so swiftly and so gracefully through the air. There are all the miracles of the little things, the beauty of the butterfly, the persistence of the ant, the thrift of the bee.

We are surrounded with wonders we cannot begin to name or number, things more marvelous than anything that ever came forth from the mind of man.

Long, long ago that wise old patriarch Job came to the same conclusion, and he said, thinking of God, "Which doeth great things past finding out; yea, and wonders without number." Job 9:10.

Surely we may say with David, "O Lord, how manifold are Thy works! in wisdom hast Thou made them all: the earth is full of Thy riches." Ps. 104:24.

Cutting the Wrong Grass

Little James is one of the dearest little boys you ever saw. If you could see him, I am sure you would want to pick him up in your arms and hug him. But, well, he is a real boy, even though he is so young, and just as full of mischief as boys usually are.

You'll never guess what he did the other day. Every time I think about it I laugh all over—though I suppose I should cry because of what nearly happened.

Well, it was this way. James was in his garden with his daddy. I chanced to be quite near, and so saw everything.

His daddy was cutting the grass with a lawn mower. On the lawn was a pair of shears.

Baby James, eager to help his daddy, picked up the shears and started cutting the grass.

"Look, Daddy," he cried, "I'm helping you cut the grass."

127

Daddy looked and smiled his thanks, but told him he should not play with the sharp shears.

"Put them down at once!" he said.

Just then Prince ran onto the lawn.

Prince is their dog, you know, a little dog with lots of hair— the kind of dog that really would look nicer if he could go to the barber and have a bob or a shingle.

At any rate, little James seemed to think so, for, leaving his grass cutting, he gave chase to Prince, shears in hand.

Unfortunately, he missed Prince's hair and caught his hind leg, and what might have happened if little James's hands had been stronger I don't like to think.

But the sight of that poor little dog walking across the lawn with the shears attached to his hind leg, and with the astonished little James looking on, is one that I shall not soon forget!

Of course, James's daddy saw it, too, which was rather unfortunate for James. What happened next it wouldn't be fair to tell you, but I rather think James will try to remember in future that it is always best to do what Daddy says, and to do it at once.

Oh, by the way, I should add that Prince still has four legs.

BTS 7-9

Jackie's Mended Yacht

Jackie was feeling so miserable he almost wished he could die. Even the presence of Chummie didn't make him feel much better, comforting though he was.

You see, there was a nice big pond in Jackie's yard, with lots of water for floating boats, and Jackie and Dickie—the little boy next door—had had the most wonderful times together there.

Then one day Jackie had brought out a beautiful new yacht that his father had given him, and, of course, Dickie had wanted to play with it too. Jackie had selfishly said No; so pretty soon there had been a quarrel. Then they had started to fight over the yacht, and while they were carrying on like this, they had both got too near the edge of the pond, and, before they could save themselves, had fallen with a great splash into the water!

What a sight they had both looked when at last they had managed to crawl out, drenched to the skin, and covered with slimy mud!

Unfortunately, it had been rather chilly the day they fell in, so both boys had caught bad colds and had had to stay in bed for several days.

131

One day Jackie had brought a beautiful new yacht to sail in the pond. Dickie wanted to play with it too, but Jackie selfishly said No.

This was why Jackie was feeling so miserable.

His beautiful new yacht was smashed. He had quarreled with his best friend, Dickie. He had a bad cold and cough, and Mamma had said that he could not go outdoors again for at least another week. Worse still, he had had to have the doctor come to see him every day, and he just hated having the doctor take his temperature, look down his throat, and thump his chest all over, just as though it were a drum!

"Oh, dear me!" he sighed, "shall I ever be better? Shall I ever be able to go out and play in the yard again? How I wish I hadn't quarreled with Dickie over that yacht! Why didn't I let him have just one turn with it? Now I suppose Dickie won't ever come over here again."

Just as he was thinking like this and feeling very, very sorry for himself, he thought he heard someone whispering his name.

"Jackie! Ssh!"

He pulled back a curtain and looked out.

Down below, under the window, was Dickie. So Dickie had got better first, and had come back to see him after all.

"Open the window," whispered Dickie. "Quietly, so no-body will hear us. I'm not supposed to be over here yet, but I just had to come."

Jackie looked around to make sure that nobody was about, and cautiously opened the window.

"Throw me a bit of string," said Dickie. "I've got something for you."

"Haven't got any string up here," said Jackie.

"Aw, look for a bit," said Dickie. "There may be something about that will do instead."

Jackie looked, and all he could find was a roll of tape in one of Mamma's dressing-table drawers.

"Will this do?" he whispered.

"Fine!" whispered Dickie. "Hold on to one end and drop the other down to me."

Jackie dropped the tape out the window, wondering what-ever it could be that Dickie wanted to send up to him.

There was a pause while Dickie tied something on the end.

"Pull away," he said presently. "And I hope everything's all right again now." Then he ran away as silently as he had come.

Jackie pulled at the tape, and to his amazement up came his lovely yacht, just as perfect as the day he first took it to the pond,

with the mast mended, and all the sails and strings in place again.

What joy! And to think that Dickie had done it, that Dickie wasn't angry with him any more!

He was just bringing the yacht in through the window when he heard a noise behind him.

"Jackie!" cried Mamma. "Whatever are you doing by that open window? You'll catch your death of cold. Haven't you been ill enough already without——"

Then she noticed the yacht.

"How did you get that?" she asked, all surprised.

"Dickie brought it," cried Jackie with delight. "Dickie did! He must have forgiven me for being cross with him. Now we can play again, can't we?"

And Jackie looked so happy, so very much better all of a sudden, that Mamma decided to forget all about the open window and her precious ball of tape that she had just spied draped over the window sill.

"I hope that after all this," she said, "you will never quarrel with anybody any more."

"I won't. Surely I won't," said Jackie eagerly, and Chummie wagged his tail so hard that he must have been trying to say, "Amen."

Paul's Lesson

Paul's great ambition in life at the moment was to make a sailing boat. He had found a piece of wood about two feet long and six inches square, and was proceeding to hollow it out with a mallet and a chisel.

If you have never done this, you have missed one of the joys of life. At any rate, Paul enjoyed it. He became so interested that he could think of nothing else. As soon as he returned from school every evening, he would rush off to his little workshop and start on his job again.

Gradually the piece of wood took shape. Little by little, chip by chip, the hole became deeper and deeper. There was not much left to do now, and soon he could nail on the deck and put up the mast and sails.

Then came the Sabbath. From his earliest years Paul had learned that this is a day to be kept holy. He had been to church on this day as far back as he could remember. Ordinary work was always laid aside. He kept his very best books to read on this day. To all the family it was a time of rest and peace.

This week, however, the Sabbath seemed to Paul to have

come at the wrong time. More than anything else he wanted to finish his boat. There were only a few days left before the holidays, and he feared that he would not have it ready in time. If only he could work just a little while longer, he would be able to finish hollowing out the hull at least.

In the morning he went to church as usual. In the afternoon, however, he told Mother that he would rather not go out for a walk with her. He would look after the house while she went out, he said.

Mother had not been gone long, however, before Paul closed the book he was reading and got up off his chair. He knew that he had not really read a line of the book. All the time he had been thinking about the boat. Something seemed to be shouting in his ears, "Boat, boat, boat!"

He wandered about the house for a little while, still uncertain what to do. Very faintly another voice said to him, "Remember the Sabbath day, to keep it holy."

Then the first voice started again, "Boat, boat, boat!"

Gradually Paul moved toward his workshop. He opened the door and looked in. There could be no harm in looking in, of course, even on the Sabbath day, he told himself.

Yes, there was the boat, just as he had left it the evening before, almost finished. Another half-hour's work, thought Paul, and the hull would be ready for the deck. What a pity to have to wait another whole day before he could touch it!

He went in, shut the door behind him, and walked over to the boat. Admiringly he stroked his hand over the smooth surface of the wood.

Then, before he quite realized what he was doing, he had

138

picked up the mallet and given one bang to the chisel. The noise resounded through the stillness of the house and made Paul just a little frightened. He looked around to make sure the door was shut.

Bang! He gave the chisel another hit.

Again he felt afraid. Would Mother hear? What would she think of him? But there, Mother was bound to be out for another half-hour. She always did go out for at least an hour's walk on Sabbath afternoons.

Bang! Out flew another chip of wood.

Paul became bolder. Every hit was a little harder. But he was still very nervous.

"Oh!" he cried all of a sudden. The mallet had missed the top of the chisel and come down on his thumbnail.

Tears filled his eyes, and he danced around the room for a minute until the pain had eased. He began to wonder whether he should have started to work on his boat, but as there was only such a little bit left to do he thought he might as well finish it.

Bang! Bang! Bang!

"Oh!" cried Paul in dismay. This time he had hit the chisel a little too hard, and it had gone right through the boat. His beautiful work was spoiled. He could have wept, for now it

139

would be difficult to make the boat completely watertight.

He was almost persuaded to stop, but the misfortune had made him desperate.

Bang! Bang! Bang! He hammered away faster than ever, fearful now that Mother might return any minute and find him there.

Then the chisel slipped and cut his hand. It was a bad cut, and Paul knew it. He wrapped his handkerchief around it and ran from the room.

140

"Mother, Mother!" he cried, "I've cut myself badly! Mother, where are you?"

Fortunately, Mother was nearing home. She heard Paul's cries some distance away, and came running to him as fast as she could.

As Mother entered the front door, Paul fell over in a faint, and it was some time before he was well enough to explain what had happened.

When he opened his eyes again he found himself sitting in one of the armchairs in the dining room. Mother was bathing his forehead with cold water.

Paul began to stare at something on the wall.

"What's the matter, dearie?" asked Mother soothingly. "Don't look so worried."

"Look," said Paul, "to think of that being in front of me now."

"What?" asked Mother, very much puzzled.

"That!" said Paul.

Mother looked and at last began to understand. For there she read the old familiar words:

"A Sabbath well spent
Brings a week of content
And strength for the tasks of the morrow;
But a Sabbath profaned,
Whate'er may be gained,
Is a certain forerunner of sorrow."

How Grandma Came for Christmas

At last the day had come to open the money boxes! How long it had taken to fill them! What hard work it had meant, what careful saving, what giving up of candy and nice ribbons and special treats! To Hilda and Mona it had seemed as if they would *never* be allowed to open them, and sometimes they had even said it wasn't worth while putting the money in.

But at last the day had come! It was a week before Christmas, and of course everybody was wanting all the money he could find for presents and new dresses and things. How glad the children were that they had heeded their mother, and kept the boxes unopened till now! Mother was right, after all.

Click! went the key in Mona's little cash box, and there inside she saw the pile of pennies, nickels, dimes, quarters, and one half dollar. What joy! She counted it all up, and Hilda counted it afterward, just to make sure it was right. Two dollars and fifty-one cents! What a lot of money for a little girl!

"Now you open yours," said Mona. "I wonder who has the most?"

Hilda's was a strange-looking money box, and it certainly held money tightly. It was such a job to get it out. She had to use a knife, but as she poked it in, out came the pennies, nickels, dimes, quarters, and two half dollars. It was a lovely sight.

"Oh!" said Mona, "you have more than I!"

"It looks like it," said Hilda. "Let's count it up. One, two, three. Why, I believe there's more than three dollars!"

And so there was. It came to $3.28. How happy they were! Never had they had so much money to spend all at once.

Then came the big question. What should they spend it on? Soon they realized how little they had really saved.

There were so many things they wanted to buy, and most of them cost more than they had saved.

Mona thought she would like to get a pretty frock, but how far would $2.51 go? Hilda's first thought was for a beautiful handbag, the kind with two pockets in the middle and a mirror. But again, how far would $3.28 go? Then they talked of other things they would like—so many things—but try as they would they could not stretch their money nearly far enough to cover all their desires.

143

"I'm getting tired of trying to decide," said Hilda. "This money is a bother."

"Do you know," said Mona, "I wonder if the trouble is that we are trying to spend it all on ourselves?"

Hilda sat very quiet and still. "Perhaps it is," she said.

"Just for fun," said Mona, "let's try to think how we could spend it on some other people."

"Mamma, for instance," said Hilda.

"Yes, or even Grandma," said Mona.

"All right. You write down what you would buy for them and I'll do the same."

So they both found pencil and paper and started to write. Hilda soon made a long list—long enough to use up her $3.28 many times over.

144

"You don't seem to have put down much, Mona," she said, looking at her paper.

"No," said Mona, "but I've got an idea! I've thought of something that would be a beautiful present for both Mamma and Grandma."

"Come on, then, let's have it," said Hilda.

"Well," said Mona, "you know how Mamma has been longing to have Grandma come down here to stay with her for a while? Well, the only reason Grandma doesn't come is that she can't afford the fare and Mamma can't afford to send it to her. Wouldn't it be wonderful if we were to send Grandma her fare ourselves, and invite her down to surprise Mamma?"

"Mona, you are a genius!" said Hilda. "I should enjoy that much more than a new handbag. Let's do it right now."

"Isn't it just lovely?" said Mona. "I'm so glad you like the idea. I'd much rather see Mamma happy than have a new dress. Let's get a pen and some writing paper. You'll write the letter, won't you?"

"All right," said Hilda. "You tell me what to say."

So together they wrote to Grandma:

"Our dear Grandma,

"We all want you very much to come down here for Christmas. Mona and I have been saving up for a long time to pay your fare, and you will find it in this letter. Don't lose it, and be sure to come soon. We shall expect you next week.

"With lots of love from Hilda and Mona."

"Oh, Mona," said Hilda when she had finished writing; "whatever will Mamma say when Grandma comes?"

"Oh, that's part of the fun. She'll be so pleased and surprised she won't know what to do with herself."

Picking up their money and putting on their coats, the two went down to the post office, bought a postal money order for $5, and mailed it to Grandma. Chuckling all over and enjoying their secret immensely, they returned home to await the big surprise.

For the next few days the girls could not settle down to anything. Every footstep made them jump, and every creak of the front gate gave them a start. They felt inside themselves that they had done something big and beautiful, not unmixed with mischief, and they just couldn't keep still.

Every now and then they would burst out laughing, for no apparent reason whatever.

Mamma wondered what could have gone wrong with them. They often had innocent little secrets they tried to keep from her, but this was rather mysterious.

Then at last came a different knock at the door.

"Hilda, there's someone at the door," called Mamma. "Go and see who it is."

But Hilda guessed that the great moment had come, and she wanted Mamma to have the surprise they had planned so long. Making up a hurried excuse, she said, "Do please go yourself, Mamma."

So Mamma hurried to the door, rather hot and bothered, —thinking it was the baker or the milkman. She opened the door sharply—and there stood Grandma, with her handbags and trunk, as if she had come to stay a month.

147

"Well, well!" cried Mamma. "Whoever—whatever! Isn't this wonderful! But how did you come? Who could have dreamed you would be here for Christmas!"

"Why, didn't you expect me?" said Grandma, equally surprised.

There was a loud chuckle in the background.

"Ah, those two young scamps," said Grandma. "I guess they are at the bottom of this."

And then came the explanations, and everybody was very happy.

After the excitement had died down, Grandma called the children to her and, slowly and mysteriously, opened her trunk.

"I'm not too old to use my fingers yet," she said, pulling

out a couple of parcels. "Here's a little dress I've been making for Mona, and I've got a wee handbag made all of beads for Hilda."

"Never!" cried the girls together, looking at each other in amazement.

"Why, don't you want them?" asked Grandma.

"Want them! I should say we do! They are just perfect," said Hilda. "But how did you know? They are the very things we were going to buy for ourselves with the money we had saved in our boxes."

"Well, did you ever!" exclaimed Grandma. "Do you know, girls," she said, "I believe the good old Book is right when it says, 'He that hath pity upon the poor lendeth unto the Lord; and that which he hath given will He pay him again.'"

149

"Daredevils"

Do you know what I can do now?" cried Maurice, running indoors excitedly.

"I can't guess," said Mother, "but you are always up to something."

"Well, at last I can ride my bicycle without putting my hands on the handle bars."

"That may be very clever," said Mother, "but I'm afraid it's not very sensible."

"Why not?" asked Maurice, rather crestfallen. "All the boys try to do it, and I can do it now better than any of them."

"Maybe you can," said Mother, "but what is the purpose of it?"

"Aw, I don't know," said Maurice; "it's lots of fun."

"I suppose it must be," said Mother, "but isn't it rather risky?"

"Risky? Oh, you're always talking about things being risky," said Maurice, rather annoyed.

"Of course, we all have to take risks sometimes," said Mother, "but why take unnecessary risks?"

150

"There's no risk in that," said Maurice. "It's easy."

"Well, I don't like your doing it," said Mother, "especially with so much traffic on the roads today. After all, what are handle bars for, if not to be used to steady yourself?"

"Oh, dear!" exclaimed Maurice, "don't worry so, Mother; it's quite all right."

With this he bounded out of the house, closing the door, I am sorry to say, with a much louder bang than usual.

A moment later he was on his bicycle again, gliding down the hill from his home, his arms folded in front of him and his face indicating supreme indifference to all his mother's caution.

Gathering speed, he glided along in great style, glancing from side to side to see whether anyone might be looking at him.

Near the bottom of the hill he spied two little girls standing at the roadside, and consequently sat up a little straighter, folded his arms a little more confidently, and tilted his chin just a little bit higher. He was not "showing off," of course, oh, dear, no! just letting the little girls see how fast a boy could ride down a hill without holding the handle bars; that's all.

What Maurice failed to see, however, was a brick lying in the road, right in the path of his bicycle. If his chin had not

151

been tilted so high, if he had not been sitting up so very straight, if he had not had his arms folded, he would have seen it easily, and everything would have been different; but there, he didn't see it, and a moment later he felt a terrific bump. The front wheel twisted, the handle bars swung right around, and before Maurice had time to think what was happening, he had crashed into the ditch at the side of the road.

Some men working near, hearing the noise, ran to see what had happened, and found Maurice floundering in mud, with his bicycle, all bent and broken, on top of him.

What a pickle he was in! Slimy water dripped from his clothes as they dragged him out, while his face, hands, and knees were red with blood from cuts and scratches.

The men were very kind, and helped Maurice up the hill again to his home, one of them carrying the wrecked machine over his shoulder.

"Oh, dear!" cried Mother, her eyes wide with alarm, as she

opened the door and looked out on the strange procession. "Whatever has happened?"

Yet she hardly needed to ask. She guessed. It was, in fact, just what she had been expecting for some time.

"My poor boy!" she said, leading Maurice indoors and starting to clean him up. "What a mercy you weren't killed."

She changed his clothes and washed his wounds, binding them up till he looked as if he had just come back from a war.

Then with Maurice at last comfortably—that is, more or less comfortably—seated by the fire, she reminded him of the little chat they had had less than an hour before.

"It is right to take risks in a good cause," she added, "such as helping people in distress, but to take risks just to gratify our vanity is very foolish. There are always people—provided others are looking on—who are ready to go and peer over the edge of a precipice; or stand on the end of a pier when the waves are dashing over and the wind is blowing hard; or drive their cars

153

at breakneck speed; or swim in the sea beyond their depth; but these are not the truly brave people. Such actions are a form of pride, not of courage. They are an effort to call attention to oneself, and so are really just cheap, tawdry, self-advertisement."

"But what has that to do with me?" asked Maurice.

"Everything," said Mother. "For a moment you were just the same as these people I have mentioned, a daredevil, and the accident that sooner or later comes to all daredevils came to you."

"Um," said Maurice. "All the same it's rather nice to ride a bike without having your hands on the handle bars."

"Maybe it is," said Mother, "but I don't think it's worth while, do you?"

Maurice mournfully surveyed his bandages.

"I don't believe it is, after all," he said.

Under the Falls

Have you ever been to Niagara Falls?
If not, I'm sure you would like to go someday, wouldn't you?

Every year hundreds of thousands of people from all over the world go to see this great sight. And they are not disappointed. No one can look at that mighty mass of water dashing helter-skelter toward the precipice, then suddenly falling through rising mists of spray upon the rocks beneath, without feeling thrilled at the grandeur of it all.

Yet most people who visit this wonderful scene never see it in the fullness of its majesty and power. To do this, you must go down underneath the falls, and let the water come right over you.

Underneath?

Yes, indeed, for somebody has cut a tunnel through the solid rock, so that visitors, after going down an elevator, can walk beneath the roaring torrent and feel the spray dash over them.

Isn't it rather wet down there? It is indeed. And, of course, you have to dress for the occasion. But you can hire the things you need right on the spot, and oh, how funny they make you look! In the picture on page 158 you can see some people in these waterproof clothes. They almost look like gnomes out of some fairy story, don't they?

Well, it is all so strange and wonderful that it seems like a sort of fairyland.

Come along with me, and look up at this marvelous sight.

Isn't it simply tremendous? There seems to be no end to the mighty flood as it comes roaring down about you, wetting you from head to foot. Water—millions of tons of it—whipped to sparkling whiteness in its downward sweep, seems to come tumbling upon you, crashing, dashing, splashing as it sweeps magnificently on toward the sea.

Looking far up through the glorious falls, you catch a

COLOR PHOTO BY THOMAS CAREY

glimpse of the sky, and suddenly the love of Jesus becomes more real. Why, of course, His love is just like this, poured out from heaven in a mighty, ceaseless, overwhelming torrent.

The Bible tells us that there is no limit to His love, for He saves "to the uttermost." Hebrews 7:25.

And it never ceases, for He loves us "unto the end." John 13:1.

Neither is there any measure to His love, for "as the heaven is high above the earth, so great is His mercy toward them that fear Him." Psalm 103:11.

Like mighty Niagara, it flows all around us, comforting us, inspiring us, and supplying all our needs, "according to His riches in glory." Philippians 4:19.

It makes me think of a beautiful hymn we often sing:

"O the deep, deep love of Jesus,
    Vast, unmeasured, boundless, free;
    Rolling as a mighty ocean
    In its fullness over me."
Have you found His love to be like that—like an ocean of
goodness and friendliness rolling right over you?
You may, if you wish.
Just stand under the falls and look up.

Sylvia's Struggle

If there was one thing more than another that Sylvia disliked, it was practicing on the piano.

She more than disliked it—she hated it.

At the moment, she was in the front room sitting on the piano stool, trying to make her fingers do what the dots on the piece of paper in front of her told them to do.

Tum-tum-tum, thumped Sylvia. Tum-a-tum-tum-tum.

"Oh, dear!" she cried, angrily. "I can't get the horrid thing right."

Tum-a-tum-a-tum-tum-tum.

"Oh!"

Bang! Sylvia slammed down the lid of the piano.

"I'll never, never practice again," she cried, jumping off the piano stool and running toward the door.

As she did so, the door opened and in walked Mamma.

"Hello, Sylvia. You haven't learned that piece yet, dear, have you?" asked Mamma.

"No, and I'm not going to," said Sylvia. "I hate practicing; I hate the old piece; I hate the old piano."

159

"Sylvia, my dear!" exclaimed Mamma. "This won't do. You mustn't give up as easily as that. You'll never get anywhere in life without a struggle. If at first you don't succeed, you must try again."

"I don't want to try again," said Sylvia, pouting.

"Well, let Mamma see what she can do with the piece."

So Mamma sat down at the piano and tried the piece over. It went so easily that Sylvia's frown gradually disappeared.

"It's easy for you," she said, "but I shall never be able to play like that."

"Of course you will, darling," said Mamma. "You'll soon be playing this piece better than I can. Anyhow, Teacher wants you to play at the school concert at Christmas."

"Me!" exclaimed Sylvia. "Me play at the school concert? Ha! ha! Wouldn't they all laugh!"

"I don't see why you shouldn't," said Mamma. "There will be other little girls there playing pieces like this, and there's no reason at all why you should let them beat you. All you need is to keep on practicing."

"Practicing!" exclaimed Sylvia. "Practicing! How I hate the very word."

"But you mustn't," said Mamma. "It only means learning by doing something over and over again."

"Over and over again," repeated Sylvia. "That's the worst of it. And somehow it never comes the same twice."

"Well, come along and try again now."

Slowly Sylvia walked over to the piano and started practicing once more, while Mamma went back to her work.

Tum-tum-tum. Tum-a-tum-tum-tum-tum—

"Oh! It's no good. I can't get it right," she cried, bursting into tears.

She felt she simply couldn't start again, and went over to the sofa to cry it out.

Perhaps she was overtired, I don't know, but soon she was asleep.

The very next thing she heard was her name being called from the platform at school. The hall seemed to be full of girls all dressed in their best. Sylvia guessed that it must be the Christmas concert.

"Sylvia Silverton," Teacher was saying, "will now play for us a delightful little sonata in D minor."

Sylvia started. Was she to play? It must be true. She looked at her dress. She had on a beautiful frock which all the girls would

admire. It would be very nice, too, going up in front of them all onto the platform. As to the piece, well, she would do her best; and it would be lovely to hear everybody clapping. Perhaps they would want her to come up on the platform again, after she had finished, to play another piece.

And now they *were* clapping. Sylvia flushed, and felt very happy as she walked up the aisle past all her friends, to the platform. Still smiling and blushing, she sat down at the piano and looked at the piece.

Horrors! It was the very piece she had hated practicing. How she wished she had learned it properly! If only she had practiced faithfully! Oh, dear! But there was no turning back now. She simply had to go on and hope for the best. Perhaps the girls wouldn't notice the mistakes.

Tum-tum-tum. Tum-a-tum-a-tum-tum-tum-tum.

"He-he-he!" came from the back of the hall.

162

"Ssh!" whispered the teacher.

Tum-tum-tum.

"He-he-he-he!" laughed somebody out loud.

"Hoo-hoo-hoo-hoo!" chortled another girl, trying hard to keep it in.

It was too much for Sylvia. In her dream she slammed down the piano lid and ran from the platform.

Bang!

"Whatever is the matter?" cried Mamma, running into the room. "Why, my dear, you've knocked the flowerpot off the window sill. Sylvia!"

"Er—er, where am I?" said Sylvia. "I thought I was at school playing at the concert."

"I wish you had been playing the piano," said Mamma, stooping to pick up the flowerpot.

"I think I shall practice after this, Mamma," said Sylvia, sighing. "It was simply dreadful. I went onto the platform and found I couldn't play at all. I'll try again, Mamma. I really will."

She did; and the concert was a great success.

Broken Crackers

Here is one of the sweetest little stories I have ever heard.

How I wish I knew the little boy's name! But I don't; so I shall just have to call him Tommy. The angels will understand.

Now, Tommy was a very poor little boy whose father was out of work and whose mother took in the neighbors' washing to earn a little money. They lived all together in one room, with Tommy's brothers and sisters, in one of the dreadful slums that used to exist in London. Yet terrible as were the conditions under which little Tommy lived, he had a heart of gold.

One Sunday afternoon, while he was playing in the gloomy, narrow street near his home, he noticed an unusual number of people going by dressed in their best clothes.

His curiosity was aroused.

"Where are they all going?" he asked his boy friends.

"Church, I suppose," said one. "Goin' to sing 'ymns and listen to a man preach."

"Shucks!" said another. "Not all them lot. They're goin' to the 'arvest festival."

164

"The what?" asked Tommy.

" 'Arvest festival, I said. Don't yer know what that is? Where they 'ave potatoes and carrots and turnips and cabbages all around the pulpit. 'Aven't yer seen one of 'em?"

Tommy confessed that he hadn't.

"Then yer'd better go along and see this one," said his friend.

Tommy thought it was a good idea, and ran off toward the place of meeting.

It wasn't a church after all, only a mission hall. He recognized it at once. "Hoxton Market Mission," said the big notice over the door. Of course, he had been there several times for meals when he was very hungry. He remembered singing there with a lot of other children and hearing a kind gentleman tell about the love of Jesus.

Mingling with the people who were entering the building, he managed at last to put his head round the front door and peep in.

HERBERT
RUDEEN

What a surprise! He had never seen anything like this before. His little friend was right. There were potatoes and carrots and turnips and cabbages all around the pulpit. And lots of other things too—apples and oranges and bananas and great big bunches of grapes and loaves of bread bigger than any he had ever seen in his life before.

"Phew!" he whistled softly in sheer astonishment, while his sparkling eyes and wide-open mouth told how surprised he was to see such a sight.

"You seem very interested in everything, my little man," said a lady with a very kind voice.

Tommy looked up fearfully, and started to run away out of the building.

"Don't run away. You can stay if you wish."

"Can I?" asked Tommy. "But what's it all about?"

"Don't you know? Why, once a year everybody brings something that has been grown in the earth to show that they remember that all good things come from God and that they are thankful for the harvest."

"Do they have to grow them themselves?"

"Oh, no. They couldn't do that here, where there aren't any gardens or fields for miles and miles. They save up their pennies and buy something. Afterward all the things are given away to people who are very, very poor."

"Does everybody have to bring something?" asked Tommy wistfully.

"Oh, no," said the kind lady. "Only those who feel able to. Some haven't any pennies at all, and Jesus understands all about that."

"Um," said Tommy, thinking. "I think I won't stay now."

166

So saying, he turned and slipped away quickly through the stream of people still coming to the mission.

He was feeling in his pocket now. Yes, there it was, his one and only penny. He had picked it up in the gutter only yesterday, and was keeping it safely hidden away for some special treat.

"Perhaps they will have something in the candy store," he said to himself. "I hope it won't be too small. Those loaves of bread are so very large."

He entered the store and looked around. Lollypops? No, they wouldn't do, not for an occasion like this. Marshmallows?

No. You wouldn't get enough for a penny.

Ah, what was that over there?

"Broken Crackers— Penny a Bag."

Crackers? Yes, they would do. They were just as much "grown in the earth" as the big loaves of bread. And this bag looked fine and big, too.

Tommy bought a bag and hastened out of the shop toward the mission.

He hadn't the courage to go in the front door, but he knew there was a back way in, and if it should be open—— It was.

He felt very nervous, fearing someone would notice him. But there were still people going in, and some through the back door, too. So he went in with them, yes, right past all the beautiful things piled up around the pulpit.

Tightly in his hot, grubby hand he held the precious bag.

"Quick!" he thought to himself, "before anybody sees."

Right beside the great big loaf he dropped the precious bag.

Nobody saw him do it, for many people were passing, and those already in their seats were too busy talking to one another.

Tommy made his way to a seat as far out of sight as possible,

and not even the kind lady who had spoken to him knew he was there.

The meeting over, he made his way back to his gloomy home, feeling a great happiness in his brave little heart.

Heaven was happier, too, I believe, as the angels brought back news of his lovely deed.

The bag of broken crackers was found, of course. The man in charge of the mission discovered it under the great big loaf, and dropped a tear as he thought of the precious, childish love that had inspired the gift.

169

He told me that he thought this was the richest gift of all.
I think it was, too, don't you?

And it made me think of a story Jesus once told about a poor
widow who went to the temple one day and saw the people giving their offerings, and "she threw in two mites, which make a
farthing."

And Jesus said to His disciples: "Verily I say unto you, That
this poor widow hath cast more in, than all they which have cast
into the treasury: for all they did cast in of their abundance; but
she of her want did cast in all that she had." Mark 12:43, 44.

170

Where Angels Weep

Thinking of Tommy reminds me of another story I have wanted to tell you for a long time.

It's about Tommy's home; or rather about the homes of hundreds of other poor little boys and girls who live in the slums of the great cities of the world.

I have been in many of them, and would like to take you along with me on a visit if you'll come. For if somebody didn't take you, I'm sure you'd never go.

If you were to go to London, you would visit the Tower and Westminster Abbey and St. Paul's. In Paris you would go to the Eiffel Tower and the Louvre and Napoleon's Tomb. In New York you would go up the Empire State Building and visit Radio City and places like that. But you would never think of going round the corner, off the bright main streets where the fine buildings and the nice stores are, to see how the poor people live.

Sometimes, though, we should go round that corner, just so we might understand something of their need, and try to think how we may help them best, yes, and be more thankful for the rich blessings God has given to us.

But see, here we are, in the very street where Tommy used to live, thirty years ago. There are no nice lawns and gardens in front of the houses. Instead, they are all joined together in long rows on both sides of the street. The front doors are close together and open right onto the pavement. There are many children playing about, some in the gutters, and all very dirty and poorly dressed. Over there is a house with the blinds pulled down. Evidently there is something the matter there. Let's go and see what it is.

Several families live in this house, each family having one room. Yes, one room for Father, Mother, and all the children. How would you like to live like that?

We knock on the door. It is opened by a very sad-looking man. He has tears in his eyes, for he has been weeping.

He takes us into a little back room. It is only nine feet square. Measure that out sometime, and see how very small it

172

is. He tells us that in this room he and his wife and three children have lived, but they are not there now. His wife has just died, also one of his children. They didn't have enough to eat; so when sickness came, they were not strong enough to resist it.

There is no furniture in this room, only a coffin, with the poor children's mamma inside.

Where are the children?

We find the two of them in the next room, asleep in the neighbor's bed. Poor little motherless things!

But look at that cat by the cupboard! How alert it is! Its whiskers are sticking straight out. And no wonder! It is waiting for the rats that come up from the sewer every night.

Ugh! I can hear you say. Sewer rats in the bedroom! Yes, but wait, there's more to show you yet.

Here is another house in the next street. It is a little larger than the first one we saw, but twenty-five people live in it.

The family we want to see lives in the basement. There are just two rooms down there—a bedroom and a kitchen. Here live a father, mother, and five children.

Let's look in the bedroom.

There are holes all over the floor, some of them covered with pieces of metal cut from cans of various kinds. They are

rat holes, and as fast as one hole is covered up, the rats make another.

See those cracks around the fireplace? At night beetles come out of those cracks, hundreds of them, and crawl all over the room.

Dreadful! I know it is, but look, there's a big old-fashioned iron bedstead over there, with one of those uncomfortable springs that sag in the middle and throw everybody into the center.

Surely nobody sleeps in there!

Oh, yes. That's the children's bed. They all sleep in it—at least four of them do—down in that dreadful dungeon among the rats and mice and beetles and many other living things, too. Poor things!

Now let's go——

But you don't want to see many more, I know. All right, then, just come with me to Tommy's mission—you know, the one where he saw the harvest festival. I want you to see how the dear people here care for the poor little ones who come to them out of these terrible homes.

Every afternoon seven hundred children used to be fed in this place. The hall will hold only five hundred; so the others waited their turn outside—sometimes in the rain!

Let's watch them awhile.

It is ten minutes to five, and the crowd of excited children are pouring in, dozens and dozens of them, all very dirty and very ragged, but, oh, so happy that in a few minutes they are going to get something to eat.

Just look at them. You never saw such a sight in all your life. On the front row there isn't one with a whole pair of shoes.

174

All of their toes are sticking through, and they have no stockings. Most of the clothes don't fit anyway, because they were bought long ago for somebody else.

Their hair is all tangled and matted, and their bright little faces are as soiled as can be. As for their noses—oh, dear, their noses!

Poor dears!

Now they can smell the food cooking. It will soon be ready. The delicious aroma brings new eagerness to every face. They can hardly wait.

A whistle is blown, and a kind gentleman speaks.

"What shall we do before we eat?" he asks.

"Say grace!" cry several.

"Yes, of course," he says. "And what else?"

"Sing!" shout others.

"Good. Let's sing, and let Jesus know how much we love Him."

Sing! Can they sing? And at such a time?

Can they? I should say they can. Though it is a long time since I last heard them, their happy songs still ring in my ears. I wish I could hear them now.

And listen. What are they singing?

> "Wide, wide as the ocean,
>   High as the heavens above,
> Deep, deep, as the deepest sea
>   Is my Saviour's love.
> I, though so unworthy,
>   Still am a child of His care;
> For His Word teaches me
>   That His love reaches me
> Everywhere."

How very beautiful! Think of their homes, their dreadful, squalid homes, and yet they sing of the love of Jesus reaching them there!

But listen again. They are singing another song now, just as sweet as the other:

> "Over and over,
>   Like the mighty sea,
> Comes the love of Jesus,
>   Rolling over me!"

176

Over and over, round and round, faster and faster they move their dirty little hands as they come, again and again, to that last wonderful line.

Look at them! Their pale, wan faces are wreathed in smiles, their mouths wide open, as they sing their loudest, "Rolling over me!"

How can they do it? Doesn't it make you wish you were as grateful for the love of God as they are?

Today the worst of London's slums have been cleaned away but in many other cities of this world thousands of boys and girls live in homes as bad as Tommy's, or even worse.

Poor little children of the slums! Should we not say a prayer for them tonight?

Children of the Darkness

Dear children of the darkness,
We think of you tonight,
And pray the dear Lord Jesus
To end your dreadful plight.

We sorrow at your suffering,
We weep for all your pain,
And pray the dear Lord Jesus
To smile on you again.

We know that in His mercy
He seeth all you do,
And pray the dear Lord Jesus
To make things up to you.

We wish that we could help you,
And all we can we will;
But soon the dear Lord Jesus
Will do it better still.

He comes again in glory
To end all sin and woe,
That those who love Him truly
Eternal joys may know.

Dear children of the darkness,
Your night will soon be o'er,
And light and love and beauty
Be yours forevermore!

UNCLE ARTHUR

Holding On

Some time ago, when visiting a large garage where buses are repaired, I noticed something which interested me very much.

Everything was on the move.

The movement was so slow that at first I did not notice it; but as I watched carefully, I began to realize that from the moment the damaged bus came in to be overhauled, it never stopped until it went out of the garage again.

That sounds funny, I know, but it is a fact; the reason being that underneath the floor there is an endless steel cable gently moving along all the time. To this each bus is attached as soon as it enters the building, and everything that is done to it happens as it passes on its way. Cleaners, painters, upholsterers, mechanics, are waiting all along the line to do their part, until at last the bus goes out on the road once more so spick and span you would think it was brand new.

Let's watch one of the old buses coming in, and see what happens to it. What a sight it is, with its fenders all dented, its paint work scratched, its windows cracked. This one has evidently been in a smashup. Everything seems to be wrong with it.

First of all, as it passes under a powerful crane, giant arms embrace the body and lift it off the chassis, which is driven off to its own section for attention.

The body, on a trolley, is attached to the ever-moving wire, and starts off on its two-day trip through the big garage.

Men appear on the scene and remove the dented fenders and the bent steel plates, and hurry them away to the foundry to get them straightened out. Other men enter the bus and start to remove the seats for recovering. Painters stand by, ready to apply the first coat of fresh paint.

Meanwhile the chassis, also gripping the ever-moving wire in its own section, is being quickly torn apart, every bolt and nut being removed, tested, and renewed where necessary. Engine, brakes, wheels, all are detached, taken to pieces, and passed through a mighty washing machine to remove all grease and

dirt. Then, as the frame moves on and on, its parts, polished all shiny bright, are returned to it.

Wheels, brakes, engine, and the rest are all replaced, and just as it begins to look the way a chassis ought to look, it sees its old body just ahead, resplendent in its coat of new paint, all ready waiting for it.

The two are reunited, and not long afterward the garage doors open, and the bus, now renovated from end to end, rolls out onto the road once more.

Just think a minute. How and why did this marvelous change take place?

Because the broken down old thing held on to the moving wire! If the bus had said to itself, "I don't want to have my old plates, my old seats, and my old fenders fixed; I don't want to have my worn-out engine taken to pieces; I don't want to put up with all this trouble; I'm not going to hold on to this wire"—well, then it would have remained just a broken down old bus, wouldn't it?

But it held on to the wire, and was changed.

And it's just that way with all of us, children. The dear Lord Jesus wants to take every life that has been spoiled by sin, and make it over again. He wants to clean up, not only the outside paint work, but every nut and bolt and screw and washer in our engines, with brakes and wheels and all the rest.

He has His own way of doing it too, and it never fails, if He is given full sway.

So if you want to be made over again, and have all the bumps and dents and scratches taken away from your character, just tell Him all about it, take hold of His love, and He will help you to become the kind of boys or girls He wants you to be.

Some things may happen that you may not like. But do not worry or become discouraged. Tell yourself it is just the dents

being knocked out, or the tiny scratches being sandpapered.

If you know you are *holding on to Jesus,* you may be sure that all will be well in the end. You may come to Him in the worst possible mess, but if you yield yourself into His hands He will make such a wonderful change in you that you won't know yourself.

Instead of thinking always of yourself you will become unselfish, ever thinking how you can help others. Anger and impatience will be replaced by gentleness. And you will never be quarrelsome again.

Indeed, there's no end to the good that will happen if you just take hold of that golden cord of love that links earth to heaven and moves ever onward and upward to the kingdom of God.

It's just a matter of holding on.

PAINTING BY RUSSELL HARLAN

The Hall of Portraits

Bruce was the eldest son of a Scottish lord, and heir to all his father's great estate.

Now he was leaving home to go to boarding school, and he and his father were having a final chat before they said good-by.

"Let us walk down the hall," said Father; "there is something I want to show you there."

Bruce had walked down that grand old hall many a time, thinking of it only as a passageway between the front entrance and the majestic ballroom at the other end of the castle, but suddenly it became something quite different.

"Look up at the walls," said Father, and Bruce, looking, saw the familiar portraits he had seen since he was a little child. They lined the walls on each side and were the work of many a famous artist.

186

PAINTING BY WILLIAM HEASLIP

"These men," said Father, "are your ancestors. It is the record of them all that they never once did a dishonorable deed. If they could speak, they would tell you they expect you to follow their example. One day, if time should last, your portrait will also adorn these walls, and it must be without disgrace. The tradition of the family must not be broken."

That was all, but Bruce never forgot. At school, at college,

Madame Marie Curie   David Livingstone   Florence Nightingale

and in afterlife the memory of that hall of portraits remained, keeping him from all pettiness and folly and ever inspiring him to great and noble deeds.

What a fine thing it would be if all of us could carry a similar glowing memory all through life!

Of course, there are not many of us who live in castles and the pictures of our humble ancestors are probably hidden away in some photograph album, or moldering in some old box in the attic. Our homes aren't big enough nowadays to have a hall of portraits; and if they were, we probably would want to hang some different kind of picture.

Yet all of us, if we will, may build up in our minds a hall of portraits of our own, hanging there the pictures of all the great and noble men we have ever known or read about, the memory of whom will help to keep us loyal and true to what we know to be right.

Whom would you put there? Perhaps the portrait of a lovely mother, a self-sacrificing father, some gallant missionary, some martyred Reformer, some fearless hero of a great crusade.

Perhaps I could make some suggestions.

Personally, I would want to start with a few of the great

188

Henry Ford   George Washington   Abraham Lincoln

Bible characters. From the Old Testament I think I would choose Moses, who freed Israel from the bondage of Egypt, and Elijah, the prophet who so gallantly championed God's cause in a time of great wickedness. Then from the New Testament I would choose the apostle Paul because of his wonderful faith and courage, and the apostle John because of his devoted love for his Master.

On another part of my hall of portraits I would display the pictures of great Reformers, beginning with John Wycliffe, known as the Morning Star of the Reformation. Beside him I would like to see John Huss of Bohemia, Martin Luther of Germany, and William Tyndale, who gave us our English Bible.

Farther on would begin my portraits of missionaries, and there I would have William Carey, the cobbler who went to India, Hudson Taylor of China, and David Livingstone and Robert Moffat, who opened up Africa to the gospel. With them, too, I would place some modern missionaries, such as F. A. Stahl, who carried the gospel to the Indians of the Amazon, and Captain Jones, who braved the cannibals of the South Sea Islands for Christ's sake.

189

Beside these I would hang the portraits of people like George Müller, who did so much for orphans; William Booth, who spent his life for the poor; Florence Nightingale, the pioneer of modern nursing; and Andrew Carnegie, who used his vast fortune to help so many.

Oh, yes, and I would want to have the portraits of some of the great explorers, too—brave men like Columbus, the discoverer of America; Shackleton and Byrd, of South Pole fame; and Colonel Glenn, the first American astronaut to orbit the earth.

I would gladly display as well some of the noble statesmen who have guided their countries through great crises, men like Gladstone, once prime minister of England, George Washington, and Abraham Lincoln.

I would also want to have some of the pioneers in science and medicine, such as Thomas Edison, who gave us electric light; James Watt, who invented the steam engine; Madame Curie, who discovered radium; Marconi, who invented wireless telegraphy; Baird, who gave us television; Fleming, who found penicillin—and many more.

And I wouldn't be forgiven if I didn't want also the pictures of men who have done much for modern engineering—like Henry Ford in the auto industry, Steinmetz, the wizard of electrical energy, and Einstein, the father of atomic physics.

Then there are great poets like Milton, who wrote *Paradise Lost;* Tennyson, who wrote that delightful poem every boy loves, *The Charge of the Light Brigade;* and Longfellow, who penned those stirring lines, *The Building of the Ship.* He wrote also *The Village Blacksmith,* and many others you love to read in school.

191

While James Watt sat in his home watching the kettle boil he was thinking. He discovered the power of steam that drives our great engines and big ships today.

There are some who would feel bad if I didn't have some great artists too, such as Michelangelo, Raphael, and Rembrandt. And what a lot of musicians also deserve a place in our hall of portraits! We could only make a start with Johann Bach, Chopin, Beethoven, and Handel, who composed the wonderful "Hallelujah Chorus."

Oh, dear! What a lot of pictures! My hall doesn't seem nearly big enough to hang them all. I am going to suggest, however, that you reserve one wall all by itself for the greatest portrait of all.

Jesus, who inspired so many of these men and women to great deeds, deserves the most beautiful picture any artist could paint, and the most prominent place in our hall of portraits. If you make His life the standard by which you judge the worthiness of all the other great men you would honor, you will never hang a picture of anyone who ever did a dishonorable deed. Then the fragrant and stimulating memory will inspire you, as they inspired Bruce, to follow in their steps, and give your life to some of the noble and heroic tasks still waiting to be done.